Unbeatable Year 3 SPaG practice from CGP!

The best way for pupils to improve their Grammar, Punctuation and Spelling in Year 3 (ages 7-8) is by doing as much practice as they can.

That's where this book comes in. It's packed with questions that'll test them on all the crucial Grammar, Punctuation and Spelling skills, including those introduced for the first time in Year 3.

And there's more! Everything is perfectly matched to the National Curriculum and we've included answers at the back. Enjoy!

What CGP is all about

Our sole aim here at CGP is to produce the highest quality books — carefully written, immaculately presented and dangerously close to being funny.

Then we work our socks off to get them out to you — at the cheapest possible prices.

Contents

Contents

Spelling

Published by CGP

Editors

Keith Blackhall, Heather Cowley, Emma Duffee, Catherine Heygate, Gabrielle Richardson, Hayley Shaw, Sam Summers
With thanks to Andy Cashmore for the proofreading.
With thanks to Jan Greenway for the copyright research.

ISBN: 978 1 78294 131 6

Clipart from Corel®
Printed by Elanders Ltd, Newcastle upon Tyne.
Based on the classic CGP style created by Richard Parsons.

Section 1 — Word Types

Nouns

Nouns **are words that** name things.

Common nouns are everyday words for things. ⟶ pizza   boy

Alice   York   Monday ⟵ **Proper nouns** are names for particular people, places or things.

(1) **Underline the** <u>nouns</u> **below.**

Tip: proper nouns always have a capital letter.

 Brazil   he    monkey    girl    quickly

 pencil   go   April    speak   Emma

(2) **Draw lines from the** <u>nouns</u> **below to the correct** <u>label</u>.

game   Tuesday

tree    Common nouns   money

London   house

dog   Rachel

Daniel    Proper nouns   America

December   book

 Now Try This   **Name five objects that you take to school. What type of word are they? Look at the box at the top of the page to help you.**

Adjectives

Adjectives are words that tell us more about a noun.

| the big car | a red scarf | an angry man |

1 Underline the **adjectives** below. Then write them on the **board**.

happy

Imani

church   sheep

quiet

girl

purple

her

small   famous

badger

clever   silly

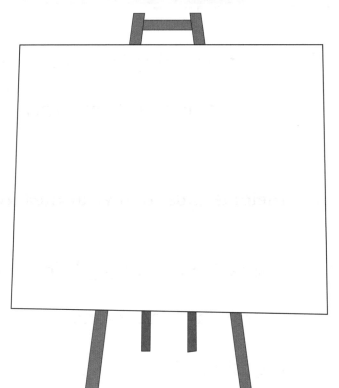

2 Use a suitable **adjective** to describe each of the pictures below.

the .... bear   the .... girl

the .... penguin   the .... carrot

 Use as many adjectives from question 1 as you can in a single sentence.

Section 1 — Word Types

Articles

Articles are the words 'a', 'an' and 'the'. They go before nouns.

Use 'a' when the noun starts with a consonant sound. ⟶ I need a holiday.

We had an argument. ⟵ Use 'an' when the noun starts with a vowel sound.

1 Circle the **article** in each sentence below.

Vowel sounds are usually made by the letters 'a', 'e', 'i', 'o' and 'u'.

I would like a hamburger.

Yesterday, we saw an alligator.

Melanie has a TV in her room.

Here's an apple.

2 Circle the correct **article** in the sentences below.

There's <u>a</u> / <u>an</u> orange in the fruit bowl.

My sister has got <u>a</u> / <u>an</u> boyfriend.

<u>A</u> / <u>An</u> cat has just run through the garden.

If it snows, we could build <u>a</u> / <u>an</u> igloo.

3 Add <u>a</u> or <u>an</u> to the sentences below so that they make sense.

Olga saw .... elephant on the way to school.

There was .... spider in the bath.

The play was .... disaster.

.... eagle flew over the houses.

Use 'the' when talking about **specific** things.

> The phone rang. ⟵ This means a **specific** phone.

Use 'a' and 'an' when talking about **general** things.

> This means any phone. ⟶ A phone rang.

4 Circle the correct **article** in the sentences below.

We went to a café and Thomas ordered <u>the</u> / <u>a</u> drink.

I would really like to go on <u>the</u> / <u>a</u> London Eye.

Matthias and Isabel had <u>the</u> / <u>a</u> great time in Italy.

He would like to know <u>the</u> / <u>a</u> truth.

Mark says this book is <u>the</u> / <u>a</u> best one he's ever read.

Jafar really needs <u>the</u> / <u>a</u> good night's sleep.

<u>The</u> / <u>A</u> view from our bedroom window is wonderful.

5 Add <u>a</u>, <u>an</u> or <u>the</u> to the sentences below so that they make sense.

When it's hot, we go out for .... ice cream.

Mum makes the best pancakes in .... world.

My computer has broken, so I need .... new one.

.... afternoon walk through the park is a lovely idea.

Harriet was excited about her trip to .... Eiffel Tower.

List the objects you can see from where you're sitting, using 'a' or 'an'.

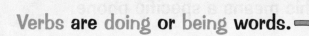

Verbs

Verbs are doing **or** being **words.**

They play video games.   We travel by car.   I am fine.

Verbs change **depending on** who **is doing the action.**

He knows a lot.   I know a lot.

① **Circle the <u>verbs</u> below and then write them on the board.**

eat

be   two

see   the

a

his

talk

write

run

sit

② **Underline the <u>verbs</u> in the sentences below.**

He has a motorbike, a car and a van.

I do my homework as soon as I get home.

Jenny and Tariq go to the cinema on Fridays.

Susie often flies to Germany to see her friends.

The supporters are happy with the referee's decision.

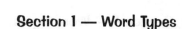

3 Circle the correct <u>form</u> of the verb in each of the sentences below.

Suma <u>enjoys</u> / <u>enjoy</u> playing tennis at the weekend.

The children <u>walks</u> / <u>walk</u> to school every day.

Craig and Will <u>takes</u> / <u>take</u> the train to work.

She <u>hates</u> / <u>hate</u> doing the washing-up.

Khalid usually <u>meets</u> / <u>meet</u> his friends in the park.

4 Add the <u>correct</u> verb from the box to the sentences below.

| lives | chases | prepare | annoys |

Ronnie .... his sister by pulling her hair.

Our dog .... the cat around the garden.

A ghost .... in the castle.

Mum and Dad .... the dinner.

5 Use the picture clues to work out each <u>verb</u>.

| | l | | y |

| | | t |

Find a book and choose a chapter from it. On a piece of paper, write down all the verbs that you can find in the chapter.

Adverbs

Adverbs are words that describe verbs.

The choir sang loudly.

Adverbs often end with -ly.

They can tell you how, when and how often the verb was done.

He played quietly.   I'll see you later.   I never eat beans.

1 Underline the <u>adverbs</u> below.

always   slowly   gently   daisy

sad   teddy   next   then

2 Circle the <u>adverb</u> in each sentence below.

The guests will arrive soon.

The dog playfully licked my nose.

He rarely goes to London.

The children greedily ate the chocolate.

Ivy always drives Mike to the shops.

Maya accidentally fell and grazed her arm.

(3) Circle the correct <u>adverb</u> to complete the sentences below.

It's our turn <u>next</u> / <u>never</u>.

Jonathan doesn't <u>often</u> / <u>soon</u> complain.

Kenzo <u>quickly</u> / <u>warmly</u> ran to the door.

Shops are <u>next</u> / <u>usually</u> open every Monday.

Calvin <u>quietly</u> / <u>brightly</u> sneaked past the house.

We <u>busily</u> / <u>perfectly</u> sorted through our things.

Violet is <u>early</u> / <u>normally</u> late for school.

The pupil <u>here</u> / <u>rudely</u> interrupted the teacher.

(4) Complete the sentences below using the most suitable <u>adverb</u> from the box. Use each adverb only <u>once</u>.

> daily   sometimes   carefully   afterwards   outside   never

I wish it was always open, but .... it's closed.

We never run out — our milk is delivered ....

Gary ate a lot — .... he felt really full.

There wasn't room inside, so I had to wait ....

My brother's lazy — he .... helps us.

Habiba .... wrapped the presents.

Can you replace the adverbs in question 2 with different adverbs?

Section 2 — Clauses and Phrases

Clauses

Most sentences are made of clauses.

A main clause makes sense on its own. ⟶ Hannah walked off.

A subordinate clause gives extra information but it doesn't make sense on its own.

Hannah walked off because she was annoyed.

    main clause   subordinate clause

(1) **Draw lines to match each <u>group of words</u> with the correct label.**

I love chips   while eating cheese

main clause

until they arrive   it's dark

when it's over   if you're coming

they told lies   **subordinate clause**   before the bell rang

he plays hockey   she's happy now

(2) **Underline the <u>subordinate clause</u> in each sentence below.**

Li drives to work when it rains.

The girls keep the light on because they're afraid of the dark.

After she had played tennis, Jean went out for dinner.

If the water rises any further, we'll have to get help.

3 Tick the sentences where the <u>main clause</u> is underlined.

I'll go swimming <u>while Timothy goes for a run</u>. ☐

Before we go out to play, <u>we need to tidy up</u>. ☐

<u>The children were soaking wet</u> because it was raining. ☐

<u>If you do that again</u>, I won't play with you any more. ☐

<u>We couldn't see the stars</u> until the sun had gone down. ☐

4 Draw lines to match each <u>main clause</u> to the most sensible <u>subordinate clause</u>.

He enjoys watching cartoons   if it stops raining.

I had a pudding   until he's feeling better.

Jane will play tennis   before the concert.

Aasir can't go to school   after my main meal.

The musicians practised   while eating popcorn.

5 Write a <u>main clause</u> next to each <u>subordinate clause</u> below.

Before we had dinner, ...

While Ishan plays the piano, ...

When Mum arrived, ...

Now Try This   Write three sentences on a topic of your choice.
Each sentence should have a main clause and a subordinate clause.

Section 2 — Clauses and Phrases

Phrases

A phrase is usually a group of words **without** a verb.

| by the lake | very sad | too late |

1 Put a tick next to the groups of words that are <u>phrases</u>.

far too early ☐   really funny ☐   he laughed ☐

very difficult ☐   before midnight ☐   Turn left. ☐

she knew it ☐   The bird sang. ☐   That's great! ☐

2 Replace the underlined <u>phrases</u> below with your <u>own phrases</u>.

Ava jumped <u>over the puddle</u>.

Ava jumped ....

The teacher spoke <u>very loudly</u>.

The teacher spoke ....

Rabbits are <u>cute and fluffy</u>.

Rabbits are ....

Now Try This

Choose two of the phrases you ticked in question 1.
Use each one in a sentence.

Noun Phrases

A **noun phrase** is a phrase that acts as a noun.
Noun phrases add extra information to sentences.

lots of biscuits   lots of yummy, chocolate biscuits

These are **noun phrases**. The noun is simply 'biscuits'.

1 Circle all the <u>noun phrases</u> below. Then write the
<u>noun</u> in each of these phrases on the clipboard.

not normally

blue shoes

quite sure

cuddly hamsters

those amazing colours

chocolate muffins

lazy elephants

so bright

all of the teachers

next to her

2 Circle the <u>nouns</u> in the underlined <u>noun phrases</u> below.

Rhiannon waved at <u>the green, hairy monster</u>.

Mum and Dad bought <u>a new leather sofa</u>.

Mr Dalal lost <u>his favourite, stripy socks</u>.

She doesn't like <u>the houses over there</u>.

 Think of your own noun phrases to replace the
underlined noun phrases in question 2.

Mixed Sentence Practice

Sentences can contain different types of clauses and phrases.

main clause   subordinate clause

Eloise ran away because she was very scared
of the horrible monster.

noun phrase

① Draw lines to match each <u>group of words</u> with the correct label.

up the mountain   I like reading

clause

let's go for a bike ride   really tall men with red hair

phrase

sandwiches are nice   a fun game

② Circle the <u>noun phrases</u> below.

the deep, blue sea

every Wednesday

terribly angry

smiling happily

extremely slowly

a very muddy path   very distant   open gently

(3) Write whether the underlined part of each
sentence below is a **main clause**,
a **subordinate clause** or a **noun phrase**.

Jenny was very happy with <u>her shiny new bike</u>.

⬆
....

<u>After the sun had set</u>, Rishi got lost in <u>the deep, dark woods</u>.

⬆ ....

⬆ ....

<u>I cut the whole loaf of bread in half</u> and put it on <u>a small plate</u>.

⬆ ....

⬆ ....

(4) Complete each sentence below with the type
of **clause** or **phrase** shown in the coloured **box**.

(subordinate clause)

I enjoyed playing football today ....

(noun phrase)

He saw ...., but he didn't like it.

(main clause)

.... when you're having fun.

Now Try This   Write a sentence of your own that contains a
main clause, a subordinate clause and a noun phrase.

Section 3 — Sentences

Statements and Questions

Statements tell you something. The person or thing doing the action usually comes before the verb.

The man is here.   Is the man here?

Tip: questions always have a question mark at the end.

You can turn some statements into questions by putting the person or thing doing the action after the verb.

① __Draw lines__ to show whether the sentences are __statements__ or __questions__.

Why is he angry?   It is a windy day.

What's the time?   **statement**   How old are you?

I work in a bakery.   **question**   When will you be back?

I am so hungry.   My mum's name is Kathy.

② __Rewrite__ these __statements__ to __change__ them into __questions__.

They are ill.   ➡ ....

You are fast.   ➡ ....

I am outside.   ➡ ....

He is alright.   ➡ ....

We are downstairs.   ➡ ....

 Now Try This Explain how you can tell the difference between a statement and a question. Then write a question of your own and a statement to answer it.

Commands and Exclamations

Commands **give** instructions or orders. **They always have a verb** that gives an order. ⟹ Put me down.   Stop that!

Exclamations **show strong feelings.** ⟹ What fun this is!

1 **Write 'C' next to the commands and 'E' next to the exclamations.**

Finish your vegetables. ☐   What a day I've had! ☐

What a huge whale that was! ☐   Fasten your seatbelts. ☐

How terrible that cake was! ☐   How clever she is! ☐

What a brilliant play we saw! ☐   Fill the pan with water. ☐

How funny you are! ☐   Share your sweets. ☐

2 **Use the words in the boxes to write commands and exclamations.**

Command

(tray the hold)   (the car stop)

....

Exclamation

(thrill a is what ! this)   (nice how ! is he)

....

Now Try This Write two commands and one exclamation you might hear while baking a cake.

Conjunctions with Main Clauses

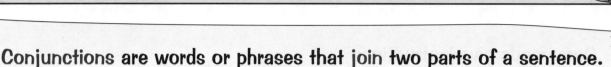

Conjunctions are words or phrases that join two parts of a sentence.

I went to the shop and I bought some bread.

first part   conjunction   second part

For, and, nor, but, or, yet and so are conjunctions which can join together two main clauses. You can remember them as the FANBOYS joining words.

For And Nor But Or Yet So

'nor' is a tricky one. It means 'but neither'.

1 Circle the <u>conjunctions</u> in the box below.

so	play	nor	your	but
up	milk	or	tree	
for	on	yet	and	the

2 Underline the <u>conjunctions</u> in the sentences below.

I want to play outside but it's raining.

Leo is going on holiday, so he needs to pack his suitcase.

We visited Grandad and we gave him his birthday present.

Tomek doesn't like sausages, nor does he like mashed potato.

Daisy can't bake cakes, yet she can bake very good biscuits.

Mr Davies is flying to France, for it's quicker than driving.

(3) Write a **conjunction** from the boxes to complete each sentence.

| for | so | and | but | or |

I want to play chess, ... Rosie wants to play too.

The zoo was closed, ... we went to the museum.

They can have ice cream .... they can have fruit salad.

The fields were flooded, ... it had rained a lot.

I don't like tomatoes, ... I do like tomato ketchup.

(4) Join the sentences below together using a **conjunction** from the box.

| or | but | and | so |

I was late. I ran to school.

....

I can't play the piano. I can play the flute.

....

We could go out. We could stay in.

....

Aanya can ride a bike. She can ride a horse.

....

Now Try This   Write four of your own sentences using the conjunctions in question 4.

Section 4 — Conjunctions and Prepositions

Conjunctions with Subordinate Clauses

There are also lots of conjunctions you can use to join a main clause to a subordinate clause.

Ella felt cold <u>after</u> she swam in the lake.

main clause — conjunction — subordinate clause

These conjunctions can also go at the start of a sentence.

After she swam in the lake, Ella felt cold.

1 Underline the <u>conjunction</u> in each of these sentences.

Before we go to America, we need to get some dollars.

I think we should play tennis if the wind calms down.

Lily crossed things off the list as her mum did the shopping.

After she finished her main course, Leah ordered a dessert.

2 Circle the best <u>conjunction</u> to complete the sentences below.

We're going to the park <u>until</u> / <u>because</u> school is closed.

Dinesh bought some cheese <u>after</u> / <u>when</u> he was at the shop.

 <u>Before</u> / <u>Because</u> the lights came on, it was very dark.

The sun was shining <u>although</u> / <u>as</u> it was cold outside.

<u>If</u> / <u>After</u> we need help, we can just ask the teacher.

3 Join the <u>clauses</u> using the <u>conjunctions</u> below.

I whisked the eggs   (even if)   we completely run out.

Let's get some petrol   (because)   we came back from camp.

We had to unpack   (before)   you paid me to do it.

I wouldn't eat a worm   (after)   Drew is better at English.

I'm good at maths   (while)   I needed them for my cake.

4 Write your own <u>ending</u> for each of the sentences below.

We usually play outside because...

....

Colin never feels very well after...

....

Mum and Dad were pleased when...

....

The football match will be cancelled if...

....

Now Try This   Look through a chapter of a book that you are reading.
How many different conjunctions can you find?

Section 4 — Conjunctions and Prepositions

Prepositions

Prepositions usually introduce a pronoun, a noun or a noun phrase.

They tell you where or when something happens. ⟹ Rob went to Scotland on Tuesday.

Prepositions can also help explain why things happen. ⟹ We were late because of the traffic.

1 Circle the **prepositions** below.

under		to	red
	on		
into		today	fox
eight			his
in	over	above	

2 Write a **preposition** to finish each sentence so it describes the picture.

The cat is .... the bed.

The bag is .... the bed.

The shoes are .... the bed.

The boy is sitting .... the table.

The lamp is .... the table.

The mouse is .... the table.

3 Underline the <u>preposition</u> in each sentence below. Then write down whether it shows <u>when</u>, <u>where</u> or <u>why</u> something happened.

Mrs Gibson burst into the classroom. ....

I brush my teeth before bedtime. ....

A mouse ran past my foot. ....

Grandpa fell asleep during the film. ....

They stayed in because of the storm. ....

4 Choose a suitable <u>preposition</u> from the box to complete each sentence.

| after | in | to | under | out of |

The Channel Tunnel goes .... the sea.

It's a long journey .... Scotland from London.

It was too late to get the train home .... the show.

I will meet you at the gate .... 10 minutes time.

Tom's toucan flew .... the window and into the garden.

5 Complete the <u>sentence</u> below. Make sure you use a <u>preposition</u>.

The squirrel jumped... .

Now Try This Describe the room you are in right now, using prepositions to explain where things are. You can look at question 2 for some inspiration.

Section 4 — Conjunctions and Prepositions

Section 5 — Verb Tenses

Present Tense and Past Tense

Use the **simple present tense** to write about something that happens regularly.

> Ian **plays** the piano.

Ian does this regularly, even if he isn't doing it right now.

Use the **simple past tense** to write about something that's finished.

> Jo **walked** to church.

To change most verbs into the simple past tense you just add 'ed' on the end.

1 Draw lines to match the <u>words</u> to the correct <u>tense</u>.

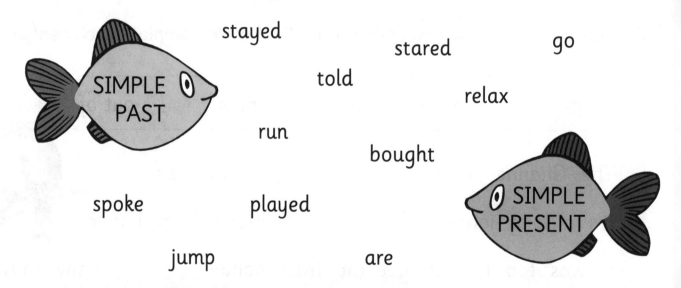

SIMPLE PAST

SIMPLE PRESENT

stayed

stared   go

told

relax

run

bought

spoke   played

jump   are

2 Complete the tables to show the <u>simple present</u> and <u>simple past</u> forms of the verbs.

Simple Present	Simple Past
I behave	I behaved
....	I offered
....	I worked
I ask	....
I hope	....

Simple Present	Simple Past
I talk	....
....	I enjoyed
I need	....
I live	....
....	I opened

Some irregular verbs are more tricky to change into the simple past tense — you just have to learn these.

I sleep a lot. ➡ I slept a lot.   I make cakes. ➡ I made cakes.

③ Rewrite the sentences below in the simple past tense.

Akari visits me.   ➡ ....

We tear it up.   ➡ ....

Alisha talks a lot.   ➡ ....

Jenny falls over.   ➡ ....

Ben packs his bag.   ➡ ....

I take the register.   ➡ ....

④ Complete the crossword by writing the simple past tense of each verb.

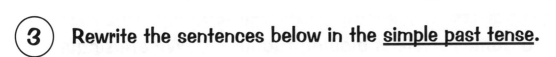

Across

1. break

2. eat

3. throw

4. read

5. dance

Down

1. beat

2. freeze

3. wear

4. dry

 Write down five more verbs in the simple past tense that don't end in 'ed'.

        Section 5 — Verb Tenses

Using 'ing' verbs in the Present

If you want to write about something that's still happening, use the present form of the verb 'to be' plus the main verb with 'ing' on the end.

am / are / is ➕ verb ➕ ing

I am talking to Sam.   He is playing rugby.   We are singing.

---

1 **Tick the sentences that show what's happening <u>now</u>. In the sentences you tick, <u>underline</u> the present form of '<u>to be</u>' and the '<u>ing</u>' verb.**

The cat is sleeping on the rug. ☐

Kieran plays football once a week. ☐

The church bells are ringing. ☐

Mrs Taylor is speaking to Miss Jones. ☐

I finish work at 5 o'clock. ☐

2 **Add the <u>present form</u> of the verb '<u>to be</u>' and '<u>ing</u>' to complete these sentences.**

The children .... laugh.......... at Mr Burgess.

My dad .... pretend.......... he's forgotten Mum's birthday.

Janice .... watch.......... the pop band 'Give This' in concert.

They .... walk.......... from Land's End to John o' Groats.

Hasan and Scott .... show.......... Lisa around the town.

> For some verbs that end in a consonant, double **the** final consonant before adding 'ing'.
>
> hop ⟹ hopping
>
> For most verbs that end in an 'e', lose **the** final 'e' before adding 'ing'.
>
> bake ⟹ baking

3 Choose a <u>verb</u> from the box and add '<u>ing</u>' to complete the sentences.

leave
race
mop
pop
take
try

My sister is .... around the track.

I am .... the party at 8 o'clock.

Jason's popcorn is .... in the pan.

Dad is .... our dog for a walk.

We are .... to find our way home.

My aunt is .... the kitchen floor.

4 Rewrite these sentences, using the <u>present form</u> of '<u>to be</u>' and the main verb with '<u>ing</u>' on the end.

A bird (to be + tap) at the window.

....

We (to be + drive) to Cardiff.

....

I (to be + invite) friends to my party.

....

 Use 'ing' verbs to write three sentences about what is happening right now.

Using 'ing' verbs in the Past

'ing' verbs in the **past** are formed like 'ing' verbs in the **present**.
You just have to put the verb 'to be' in the **past tense**.

 was / were **+** verb **+** ing

Watch out for spelling changes.

I was talking to Sam.   We were singing.   I was sitting down.

(1) Complete these sentences using the <u>past tense form</u> of '<u>to be</u>' and one of the <u>verbs</u> below with '<u>ing</u>' added.

drop

make

listen

play

clean

Harry .... tennis outside.

They .... paper planes.

I .... Kyle off at home.

She .... her bedroom.

We .... to music.

(2) Rewrite these sentences, using the <u>past form</u> of '<u>to be</u>' and the main verb with '<u>ing</u>' on the end.

Remember, some spellings change when ing is added.

I (to be + help) Jake.

....

Nawaz and Zara (to be + chase) Marcus.

....

We (to be + put) up pictures.

....

 Now Try This

Imagine that this time last week you were on another planet.
Use 'ing' verbs to describe what you were doing.

The Present Perfect

You can use the present perfect to talk about something that happened recently.

I have borrowed it.

It is formed from the present tense of 'to have' and the past tense form of the main verb.

It has snowed.

The main verb is usually the same as the normal past tense.

They have ignored me.

1 Underline the sentences below that use the **present perfect**.

I ate vegetables.

Jim has followed me.

She has arrived.

I have scratched my glasses.

He went away.

Efua has explained it.

We played cards.

Sue has talked to Phil.

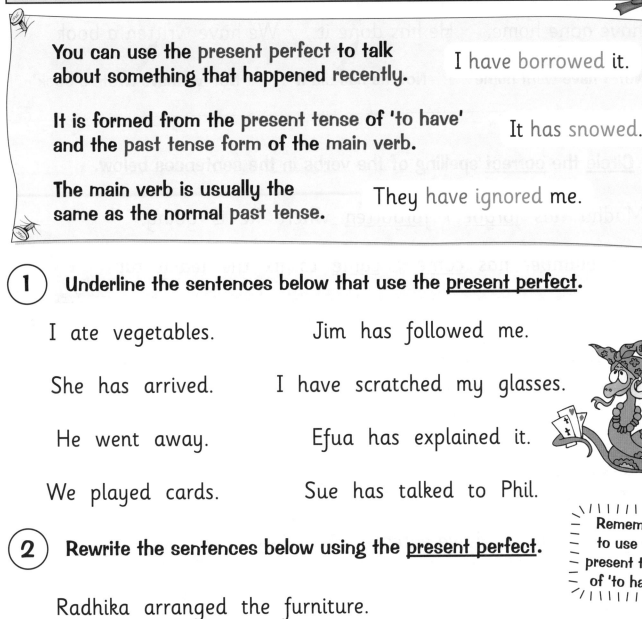

2 Rewrite the sentences below using the **present perfect**.

Remember to use the present tense of 'to have'.

Radhika arranged the furniture.

....

I finished my homework.

....

Somsak married Victoria.

....

We painted the walls.

....

Section 5 — Verb Tenses

Some **main verbs** are **different** in the **present perfect**.

I have gone home.   He has done it.   We have written a book.

Not 'I have went home'   **Not 'he has did it'**   **Not 'we have wrote a book'**

(3) <u>Circle</u> the <u>correct</u> spelling of the verbs in the sentences below.

Madhu has <u>forgot</u> / <u>forgotten</u> where he is going.

The plumber has <u>come</u> / <u>came</u> to fix the leaky tap.

I have <u>stolen</u> / <u>stole</u> an extra biscuit from the tin.

My brother has <u>drank</u> / <u>drunk</u> all the orange juice.

The sun has <u>rose</u> / <u>risen</u> in the sky.

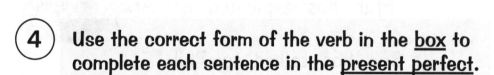

(4) Use the correct form of the verb in the <u>box</u> to complete each sentence in the <u>present perfect</u>.

(eat) I .....have eaten..... too many sweets.

(blow) The wolf .... the house down.

(thank) Bob .... everyone.

(show) We .... them our idea.

(give) My sister .... me her clothes.

(keep) They .... the money safe.

(enjoy) We .... the holiday.

(break) I .... my new game.

(cheat) The boys .... at cards.

Section 5 — Verb Tenses

5 For each verb, write the <u>simple past tense</u>.
Then, write the <u>present perfect</u>.

	Simple Past Tense	Present Perfect
see	I saw	I have seen
take		
hide		
grow		

6 Put a <u>tick</u> next to the sentences that <u>make sense</u>
and put a <u>cross</u> next to the ones that <u>don't</u>.

Rosa has been to the zoo. ☐   Izzy done the dishes. ☐

The boys seen Darren's car. ☐   I have been outside. ☐

I have came to visit you. ☐   We have seen her. ☐

Miles has done lots today. ☐   Helen has come too. ☐

<u>Rewrite</u> the sentences you <u>crossed</u> using the present perfect.

....

....

....

 Use the verbs from question 5 to write four sentences in the present perfect.

 ✓   ✓   ✓

Staying in the Same Tense

The verbs in a sentence should usually be in the same tense.

Yesterday we went to the park and we ate an ice cream.

1 **Circle** the **correct** form of the **underlined verbs** in the sentences below.

We go round to Sally's and <u>took</u> / <u>take</u> her to the shops.

Yesterday, we drove to France and <u>buy</u> / <u>bought</u> some food.

I eat muesli for breakfast and I <u>had</u> / <u>have</u> soup for lunch.

On Monday, I made a cake and <u>bake</u> / <u>baked</u> bread.

Sometimes I like to <u>pretend</u> / <u>pretended</u> I am a superhero.

2 **Tick** the sentences where the **verbs** are all in the **same tense**.

Last month I bought a book and I finished it in one day. ☐

I helped around the house and then I play outside. ☐

Dad jogged to work every day until he gets injured. ☐

I keep my room tidy but my twin leaves stuff everywhere. ☐

Yesterday, I found fifty pence and spend it on sweets. ☐

I rushed to school this morning and forgot my sports kit. ☐

3 Choose a <u>verb</u> to complete each of the sentences below.

(made)   (listen)   (licked)   (cries)

(cried)   (lick)   (make)   (listened)

I quickly .... my lolly before it dripped onto the floor.

Niall was being rude so Mrs Simon .... him stay behind.

I spend time with my sister and we .... to music.

We watched a sad film at the weekend and my mum ....

4 There are some <u>mistakes</u> in the tenses in the passage below. <u>Circle</u> the <u>verbs</u> that are in the <u>wrong tense</u>, and write the <u>corrections</u> below.

Last week, we went to Spain and (have) a great time. We

.... had ....

travel by plane and stayed in a hotel. The adults swim in

....

the sea and the children play in the pool. One day we went

....

surfing and I fall off a lot! I was sad when we leave Spain.

....

Now Try This — Write a passage that uses all four of these verbs: to see, to point, to gasp, to laugh. Make sure all the verbs are in the same tense.

Section 5 — Verb Tenses

Section 6 — Sentence Punctuation

Capital Letters for Names and I

Proper nouns **are the** names **of particular** people, places **or** things. **They always start with a capital letter.** Months, days of the week **and** countries **all need capital letters.**

| Hugo | France | Big Ben | May | Friday |

1 Circle the words below which should start with a **capital letter**.

neighbour	dog	geoffrey	potato
italy	buckingham palace	april
thursday	lake	weekend	mr smith

2 Put a **tick** next to the phrases which use **capital letters** correctly and put a **cross** next to the ones that **don't** use them correctly.

25 church street ☐   croissants from France ☐

my friend Jameela ☐   the beach in august ☐

the train to London ☐   football on Saturday ☐

the book by roald dahl ☐   miss hamilton's class ☐

Rewrite the incorrect phrases with capital letters in the right places.

....

....

....

....

You always need a capital letter to say 'I'.

My twin sister and I look alike, but I have shorter hair.

3) Circle all the letters that should be <u>capital letters</u> in this passage.

Last weekend, my brother oliver went hiking with his friends,

lydia and marc. On saturday, they climbed up snowdon, the

tallest mountain in wales. Although it rained all day, they

said that they had a great time. They want to go again in

september, but i won't go with them because i don't enjoy hiking.

4) Rewrite the sentences below with <u>capital letters</u> in the correct places.

Luckily, i asked freida to help me.

....

Miss jones said i could be king john in the play.

....

On saturday, i watched england play football.

....

Every june, i go camping in ireland.

....

Read this sentence: 'On <u>Saturday</u>, <u>I</u> am going to <u>Paris</u> with my friend <u>Harry</u>.'
Can you explain why each underlined word has a capital letter?

Section 6 — Sentence Punctuation

Capital Letters and Full Stops

You need to start each sentence with a capital letter. ⟶ My grandma loves to knit.

Sentences usually finish with a full stop.

(1) Add <u>full stops</u> to punctuate each pair of sentences correctly.

These are apple tarts Those ones are lemon

Imran didn't go to school today He was ill

I love maths I don't like drawing

My mum's bike is black My dad's is white

(2) The words in these sentences have been jumbled up. <u>Rewrite</u> the sentences in the <u>correct order</u> and add <u>capital letters</u> and <u>full stops</u> in the correct places. The first one has been done for you.

is our blue house

.Our house is blue.
....

film funny is the very

....

a ate mouse biscuits those

....

lost we in got woods the

....

(3) **Rewrite these sentences with <u>capital letters</u> and <u>full stops</u> in the correct places.**

There are two sentences on each line.

we finished the puzzle it was easy

....

it was late the shops were closing

....

my sister loves football my dad prefers rugby

....

(4) **Use your <u>own words</u> to <u>complete</u> these four sentences. Make sure you use <u>capital letters</u> and <u>full stops</u> in the correct places.**

My house is ....

.... a cheese sandwich.

We watched ....

.... a blue sports car.

(5) **Write <u>three</u> sentences. Each sentence should use one of the words below. Include <u>capital letters</u> and <u>full stops</u> in the correct places.**

lizard ....

clown ....

violin ....

Now Try This Look at these words: grumbled, ostrich, surfing. How many sentences can you make that use all of them? Remember to use capital letters and full stops.

Question Marks

Every question should end with a question mark.

| Where did he go? | Why are you laughing? |

Questions often start with question words.
Here are some common ones.

who | what | where | why

1 Draw a line to match each of these sentences to the correct <u>punctuation mark</u>.

I know who that is

What colour is your living room

Do you like reading

Which way should we go

I'll go if there's free ice cream

2 Write a <u>question word</u> from the box to complete the questions. Use each question word <u>once</u>.

.... did you put my coat?

.... is your brother's name?

.... are you telling me off?

.... much fruit do you eat?

.... wants to play chess?

.... is your birthday?

When   Why
Where   Who
What   How

3 Draw a line to <u>match</u> the <u>two parts</u> of these questions so that they make sense.

Where are   the race?

What is   my shoes?

Who won   she arrive?

When did   the dog called?

4 Write <u>a question</u> to match each of the answers given below.

Q: ....

A: My name is Anele.

Q: ....

A: I was born on the 18th of April.

Q: ....

A: I live in Birmingham.

5 Write three <u>questions</u>, using one of the word pairs below for each one.

cake   apple ....

bike   car ....

park   fair ....

Now Try This What would you ask your hero if you met them? Write three questions.

Exclamation Marks

You can sometimes finish your sentences with an exclamation mark.

Use an exclamation mark to show that something was said loudly. → "Watch out!" I cried.

You can also use exclamation marks to show strong emotions, such as anger, fear or surprise. → There's a snake in the house!

1 Complete each sentence with the <u>correct punctuation</u>. Four sentences end with an <u>exclamation mark</u> and three end with a <u>full stop</u>.

We need to hide quickly........

Asher ordered a pizza and some garlic bread........

We've won the lottery........

Just leave your shoes by the door........

Ow, that hurts........

They thought about which film to watch........

There's a shark behind you........

2 Tick the sentences which are likely to end with an <u>exclamation mark</u>.

Give me that now ☐   I brought a waterproof ☐

Watch out ☐   Stop fighting ☐

She has blonde hair ☐   Catch that thief ☐

Mix the flour and butter ☐   Try this pair on ☐

3   Add <u>full stops</u> and <u>exclamation marks</u> into the boxes in this passage. There are four missing exclamation marks and three missing full stops.

As soon as Dad stepped through the door,

we all jumped out from our hiding places ☐

"Surprise ☐" we shouted ☐

"Blimey ☐" he exclaimed, putting his hand to his chest,

"I nearly jumped out of my skin ☐"

"Happy birthday, Dad," I said, handing him his present ☐

"It's amazing ☐" he cried as he opened it.

4   Complete each sentence so that the words spoken need an <u>exclamation mark</u>.

Speech should always begin with a capital letter.

" .... !" the witch snapped.

" .... !" she cried.

"Hurry, Eva, before .... !"

"If we wait any longer... !"

I screamed at the top of my lungs, " .... !"

5   Write a sentence using an <u>exclamation mark</u> to go with the picture.

....

Now Try This   Write three sentences that you might say if you saw a dragon. Each one should end in an exclamation mark.

Section 6 — Sentence Punctuation

Sentence Practice

Remember that all sentences start with a capital letter, and you can use a full stop, a question mark or an exclamation mark to end them.

1 Match each sentence with its most likely <u>final punctuation</u>.

Who are you waiting for

Come here, right now

What great news that is

How do you get to school

What time is the film on

I'm playing football tonight

My mum's name is Rachel

I really can't believe it

2 Rewrite the sentences with the <u>correct punctuation</u>.

i'm going to scotland on friday

....

there's a ghost in this house

....

when is Nabila's birthday

....

was catarina born in portugal

....

mr baker moved to australia in may

....

3 Write the most likely <u>final punctuation</u> in each box.

You've won ☐   Custard is yellow ☐

Where are we going ☐   Let me go ☐

I'm friends with Anjali ☐   Why did you leave ☐

She crept down the stairs ☐   Ow, that hurts ☐

4 Add the missing <u>full stops</u>, <u>question marks</u> and <u>exclamation marks</u> into the boxes in the passage below.

"I opened my safe," the duke wailed, "and it was gone ☐ "

The detective made a note in her notebook and looked at the

duke ☐ He was in his silk pyjamas, gently stroking his pet cat ☐

"Did anyone else know the code to the safe ☐ " she asked ☐

"Only my butler," the duke said, "but why would he want to steal

Fluffy's diamond collar ☐ "

5 Write two sentences that end with a <u>full stop</u> to match this picture.

....

....

Write one sentence that ends with a <u>question mark</u> to match this picture.

....

Make up three sentences about crocodiles. One sentence should end with a full stop, one with a question mark and one with an exclamation mark.

Section 7 — Commas

Writing Lists

Commas are used to separate items in a list.

I play football, rugby, cricket and tennis.

You need commas between all the things in the list except the last two.
You need to put 'and' or 'or' between the last two things.

1 Tick the sentence which uses <u>commas</u> correctly.

Elena speaks, English Italian Spanish and French. ☐

Elena speaks English, Italian, Spanish and French. ☐

Elena speaks English, Italian, Spanish and, French. ☐

2 Each of these sentences is missing one <u>comma</u>.
Add one comma to each sentence to make it correct.

Tyler loves ☐ to ☐ sing ☐ act and dance.

Kofi's jumper ☐ is ☐ red ☐ orange and yellow.

Nadeem ☐ never eats crisps ☐ sweets or ☐ chocolate.

3 Write out Emil's shopping list using <u>commas</u> in the correct places.

Emil needs to buy ....

....

and ....

Emil's List
tomatoes
bananas
carrots
potatoes

4 Rewrite the sentences below with <u>commas</u> in the correct places.

Are your eyes green blue or brown?

....

The zoo has tigers lions zebras and rhinos.

....

Saskia likes to read draw paint and sew.

....

5 Add <u>commas</u> in the correct places in the paragraph below.

My best friends are Dylan Nasir and Logan. Dylan is funny friendly and chatty. Nasir is very sporty. He likes swimming cycling and hockey. Logan likes animals. His family have cats dogs and rabbits. He wants to be a vet when he grows up.

6 Write a list of <u>four words</u> to describe each of the pictures below. Remember to use <u>commas</u> in the correct places.

The socks are ....

....

The kitten is ....

....

Now Try This   Finish this sentence: "The subjects I've studied at school today are..."

Section 7 — Commas

Writing Longer Lists

Sometimes you use several words to write about each thing in a list.

> We ordered two double cheeseburgers, eight chicken nuggets, three strawberry milk shakes and some chips.

You still need to put a comma between each thing in the list.

1 This sentence is missing three commas.
Add the three commas in the correct places.

I don't like ☐ eating my ☐ vegetables ☐

doing my homework ☐ cleaning my

bedroom ☐ going to bed ☐ early or ☐

getting up ☐ for school at 7 o'clock.

2 Add commas in the correct places in the sentences below.

> Yosef needs to buy a pint of milk a bag of apples a loaf of bread and a tin of baked beans.

> I still need to have a wash comb my hair get dressed eat my breakfast and brush my teeth.

> Mia asked for a red mountain bike a pair of trainers and a book about dinosaurs.

> I watched a film helped my mum make lunch played with my brother and went to my gran's for tea.

3 Use the items below to <u>complete the lists</u>. Each list should have four things in it. Remember to put <u>commas</u> in the correct places.

500 grams of sugar   a good book   half a dozen eggs   a beach ball

a big towel   a kilogram of flour   a spoonful of honey   a bottle of sun-cream

For this recipe you will need ....

....

....

In my beach bag I have ....

....

....

4 Write a sentence describing <u>four things</u> that you want to do this weekend. Remember to use <u>commas</u> in the correct places.

This weekend I want to ....

....

....

Now Try This Write a list of your favourite things, using commas in the right places. Include at least five things in your list.

Section 8 — Apostrophes

Apostrophes for Missing Letters

Apostrophes are used to show where letters are missing from a word.

I am ➡ I'm   had not ➡ hadn't   you are ➡ you're

Sometimes the shortened word doesn't quite match the words it's made from.

will not ➡ won't

1 Draw lines to match the <u>pairs</u> of words with their <u>shortened</u> versions.

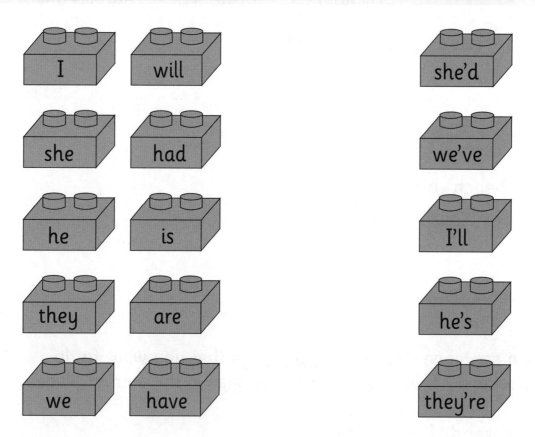

I   will

she   had

he   is

they   are

we   have

she'd

we've

I'll

he's

they're

2 Shorten these words using an <u>apostrophe</u>.

was not ....   that will ....

it will ....   where is ....

did not ....   we are ....

3 Put a <u>cross</u> next to the sentences where the <u>underlined word</u> needs an <u>apostrophe</u>.

<u>Dogs</u> love to go for walks. ☐   That <u>rabbits</u> got big ears. ☐

My <u>goats</u> called Susan. ☐   <u>Snakes</u> are often slimy. ☐

We have <u>pigs</u> on our farm. ☐   Your <u>cats</u> beautiful. ☐

His <u>hamsters</u> got spots. ☐   My two <u>rats</u> got a new toy. ☐

4 Write out the <u>underlined word</u> in each sentence as <u>two words</u>.

<u>We'll</u> have to try again tomorrow.   ....

Mrs Smith <u>doesn't</u> wear any socks.   ....

<u>She's</u> always reading a book.   ....

<u>They've</u> been on holiday again.   ....

5 Rewrite these sentences using the <u>shortened</u> version of each pair of <u>underlined words</u> and an <u>apostrophe</u>.

<u>They are</u> the best netball team.

....

<u>It is</u> raining and <u>I am</u> getting wet.

....

<u>That is</u> the biggest cake <u>I have</u> ever seen!

....

Now Try This How many shortened versions of words can you write down in two minutes? Remember to include apostrophes in the right places.

Apostrophes for Single Possession

An apostrophe and 's' shows that something belongs.

Hugo's racket ⟸ This means the racket belongs to Hugo.

(1) Write down what **each person has** using an **apostrophe** and **'s'**.

Amar ✚ 🍌 ➡ .... Amar's bananas ....

Lucy ✚ 🧸 ➡ ....

Elena ✚ 🍎 ➡ ....

Robert ✚ 🍇 ➡ ....

Zahra ✚ 🌻 ➡ ....

(2) **Cross out** the **phrases** which **don't match** the statement on the left.

belonging to the teacher ➡ (the teacher's) (~~the teachers'~~)

belonging to the cat ➡ (the cats) (the cat's)

belonging to my sister ➡ (my sisters') (my sister's)

belonging to her friend ➡ (her friend's) (her friends)

If a name ends in 's' already, you still need to add an apostrophe and an 's'. ⟶ Tomoko's hat

This rule is the same for any noun ending in 's'. ⟶ the walrus's tusks

3 <u>Tick</u> the box next to the sentences that use <u>apostrophes correctly</u>.

My boss' desk is always tidy. ☐

Thomas's painting is the best in the class. ☐

The dress's stripes are blue and purple. ☐

The class' play is about a robot. ☐

4 Rewrite the phrases with an <u>apostrophe</u> and an '<u>s</u>' to show that something belongs.

The room has furniture .... The room's furniture ....

The man has a house ....

The cactus has spikes ....

The castle has a moat ....

The suitcase has handles ....

The bus has seats ....

The bicycle has wheels ....

The keyboard has keys ....

Now Try This "Bens badgers ate all his brothers biscuits." Where should the apostrophes go in this sentence? Explain why each one is needed.

 ☑ ☑ ☑

Section 8 — Apostrophes

Its and It's

The words 'its' and 'it's' mean two **different** things.

its $\longrightarrow$ This means 'belonging to it'. $\longrightarrow$ The dog ate its tea.

it's $\longrightarrow$ This means 'it is' or 'it has'. $\longrightarrow$ It's a stormy day.

1 **Tick the boxes** next to the sentences which use '<u>its</u>' or '<u>it's</u>' **correctly**.

Oh no, <u>it's</u> a really hard maths test! ☐

I've got a new toy and <u>its</u> a train set. ☐

The bird sang <u>its</u> happy song. ☐

<u>Its</u> only been ten minutes so far. ☐

I practise writing because <u>it's</u> tricky. ☐

The lion licked <u>it's</u> lips and roared. ☐

2 **Circle** the **correct** word in brackets in each sentence below.

Do you think (its / it's) far to go?

The rat lost (its / it's) way.

The bird flapped (its / it's) wings.

I can't believe (its / it's) over.

(Its / It's) great to be on holiday.

(Its / It's) a big mess in here.

The cat licked (its / it's) fur.

The ant carried (its / it's) leaf.

3 Draw a line to match each sentence to the correct version of 'its' or 'it's'.

Look, I think **?** a plane!

My hamster loves **?** ball.

? all about taking part.

Well done, **?** going well.

The castle opened **?** gates.

? been a very long day.

We should find **?** owner.

? been ages since he left.

its

it's

4 Write down whether 'it's' means 'it is' or 'it has' in each sentence.

Thank you, it's a lovely present. ....

It's been an awful weekend. ....

It's taken ages to make this cake. ....

I think it's going to snow today. ....

I love my jumper because it's warm. ....

I wonder if it's time to go home yet? ....

It's just begun to snow outside. ....

I can't believe it's only 8 o'clock! ....

 Write one sentence that uses 'it's' and one sentence that uses 'its'.

Section 8 — Apostrophes

Apostrophe Practice

Remember that apostrophes can be used to show where letters are missing from a word, or to show that something belongs.

don't! ⇐ This means 'do not'.   Raj's book ⇐ A book belongs to Raj.

1 Fill in the <u>gaps</u> with the <u>short</u> and <u>long</u> versions of the words.

I am	.... I'm ....
....	you'll
are not	....
we had	....
....	doesn't
they have	....

2 <u>Write out</u> the <u>underlined words</u> with an <u>apostrophe</u>.

<u>Linas</u> painting   ....   the <u>moons</u> glow   ....

the <u>mans</u> bag   ....   <u>Marias</u> handbag   ....

3 <u>Tick</u> the sentences which use <u>apostrophes correctly</u>.

Stop it! Thats' not fair! ☐   It's been a great show. ☐

You're my best friend. ☐   What's the time, please? ☐

I'ts best to keep quiet in class. ☐   That is'nt my rucksack. ☐

She's not very nice to me. ☐   The train blew it's whistle. ☐

4 <u>Some</u> of the underlined words need apostrophes.
Add the <u>apostrophes</u> where they are needed.

> Be careful — not all the underlined words need apostrophes.

Do you need <u>S a m s</u> help?

The <u>b a g s</u> are all packed.

How many <u>g i r l s</u> are here?

This <u>r u g s</u> got a nice pattern.

This <u>t i n s</u> lid is stuck.

The <u>e x a m s</u> going to be fine.

These <u>f l o w e r s</u> smell lovely.

That <u>p l a t e s</u> got egg on it.

5 <u>Draw lines</u> to show <u>why</u> the <u>underlined words</u> need an <u>apostrophe</u>.

We <u>can't</u> get a seat on the bus.

The <u>door's</u> handle is broken.

My <u>hat's</u> bobbles are pink.

<u>When's</u> the circus coming?

<u>It's</u> kind to share with others.

to show possession

for missing letters

6 <u>Rewrite</u> each <u>underlined word</u> with an <u>apostrophe</u> in the right place.

That <u>trees</u> branches are very wide. .... tree's

The <u>dogs</u> coat is white with black spots. ....

Mr Wilson, <u>Ive</u> got a great idea! ....

Be careful with that or <u>youll</u> break it. ....

Tomorrow <u>wed</u> like to go fishing, please. ....

 Now Try This — "The hat belonging to Lois must not get wet." Can you rewrite this sentence using an apostrophe for possession and an apostrophe for missing letters?

Section 8 — Apostrophes

Section 9 — Inverted Commas

Inverted Commas

Inverted commas **show when someone is speaking.**
They are also called speech marks.

Inverted commas go at the
start and end of the speech. → "I'd like a cake," said Matthew.

There's always a punctuation mark before the final speech marks.

① **Tick the sentences that use inverted commas <u>correctly</u>.**

"Please may I have a sandwich? asked" Ava. ☐

"Please may I have a sandwich? asked Ava." ☐

"Please may I have a sandwich?" asked Ava. ☐

"Add some salt to the soup, said the chef." ☐

"Add some salt to the soup," said the chef. ☐

"Add some salt" to the soup, said the chef. ☐

② **Complete the sentences by adding <u>inverted commas</u> to each one.**

" I've got new spotty wellies , said Nasreen .

" Art is my favourite subject , said Bryony .

" My mum's name is Jackie , I said .

" Mushrooms are slimy and horrible , said Dan .

" I'm going to explore the attic next , said Ruby .

3 These sentences have <u>too many inverted commas</u>.
<u>Circle</u> the <u>correct</u> inverted commas in each sentence.

"I've left my "lunch at home," said Nathan."

"My "mum is getting married," said" Rosie.

"When can "we go outside?" asked" Nasir.

"We're "having a party soon," said Alex."

"Please can we have pasta "for tea?" asked Maya."

"Be careful" with that!" shouted Mrs Wilkins."

"Are you posting that "letter?" asked" David.

4 Add the <u>inverted commas</u> in the <u>correct boxes</u> to punctuate the sentences below. The first one has been done for you.

["] You can't [ ] boss me around, ["] said Aisha. [ ]

[ ] Can you give [ ] me some advice? [ ] asked [ ] Noor.

[ ] I'm going to win the race, [ ] said [ ] Alison. [ ]

[ ] Yes, [ ] I'd love to go, [ ] replied Matteo. [ ]

[ ] There's a hole in my shoe! [ ] said [ ] Kirsty. [ ]

[ ] Let's go [ ] and play in the snow, [ ] said Luca. [ ]

Now Try This Use inverted commas to write down three things that you might hear people say in a playground.

Punctuating Speech

Inverted commas go at the start and end of the speech.
The first word that is spoken always has a capital letter.

capital letter

"Your hair is messy," he said.

speech marks

capital letter

Katie said, "We're going away."

speech marks

1 Circle the words which should have a <u>capital letter</u> in these sentences.

Sam asked, "(do) you need anything from the shop?"

Tamara said, "this is going to be the best show ever!"

Anjali said, "you can be the blue piece and I'll be the red one."

"no, we don't have any red fabric, sorry," replied the man.

Tony asked, "excuse me, where is the football match?"

"we could build a raft to get across the river," said Martha.

2 Tick the sentences where the speech is <u>punctuated correctly</u>.

Harini "asked, Where's the nearest bus stop?" ☐

"Have you put your shoes on yet?" I asked. ☐

Frankie said, "No, I haven't got any more." ☐

Kit shouted, "you're going the wrong way!" ☐

"I bet you can't catch me!" yelled Femi. ☐

3 Add <u>inverted commas</u> to the <u>correct places</u> in these sentences.
Then <u>circle</u> the missing <u>capital letter</u> and <u>join it</u> to the <u>correct star</u>.

e.g. Serge said, "ⓦe're going on a bear hunt."   ☆ A

Ben asked, is this the way to the circus?   ☆ W

Emily said, all the best players practise.   ☆ D

Mikel replied, yes, I would love to come.   ☆ Y

Henry asked, do I have to eat my apple?   ☆ O

Pasha said, our dad is taking us to the ballet.   ☆ I

4 Write out these sentences with <u>inverted commas</u> and <u>capital letters</u>.

We said, you can play with us if you don't cheat.

....

The queen shouted, bring me my crown!

....

The girl asked, please may I have a go?

....

Write out a conversation between a mouse and a cat.
Punctuate the conversation with speech marks and capital letters.

                       Section 9 — Inverted Commas

Direct and Reported Speech

You only use speech marks if you're writing down exactly what someone has said. This is called direct speech.

"I love tea," said Rob. ← This is direct speech — it's exactly what Rob has said.

If you're just talking about what someone has said, you don't need speech marks. This is called reported speech.

Rob said that he loves tea. ← This is reported speech — it's just reporting what he said.

1 Draw a line to show whether each of these sentences is <u>direct speech</u> or <u>reported speech</u>.

"You can borrow it if you like," said Guy.

I asked, "How are we getting there?"

Zack said he's playing rugby later.

"We had a quiet day," Jim told them.

I heard Laura say she would help me.

"I think we should take a break," I said.

direct speech

reported speech

2 Tick the boxes next to the sentences which <u>need inverted commas</u>.

Are you coming to the playground? asked Flora. ☐

The dinosaur said he'd like to come for tea. ☐

Anya said, I've had a great idea for the fair. ☐

My mum told me not to speak to strangers. ☐

(3) Write these sentences onto the <u>whiteboard</u> to show whether they are <u>direct speech</u> or <u>reported speech</u>.

Ron asked a question.   Luna talked a lot.

"Come here!"

"Are we there?"   "I love you."

George says he's tired.

Direct speech	Reported speech
....	....
....	....
....	....

(4) Add <u>inverted commas</u> into the sentences that <u>need them</u>. The first one has been done for you.

"My favourite jam is strawberry," Charlotte told me.

Molly asked the teacher when lunchtime was.

Asaf said he hadn't taken the last chocolate.

Yes, we have lots of crayons in the tin, said Dad.

Luke said, I'm learning to play the piano.

My brother Alfie says he's going to be a doctor.

That was the best birthday ever! I said happily.

 Now Try This Look through a fiction book you are reading. How many examples of direct speech and reported speech can you find in the first half?

Section 10 — Paragraphs and Layout

Paragraphs

Paragraphs are used to group together sentences about the same:

| time | person | subject |

Grouping ideas together like this makes your writing easier to read.

1 Tick the **correct reasons** for starting a **new paragraph**.

When you get distracted. ☐

When you're writing about a different time. ☐

When you're writing about a new place. ☐

Every time you use the word 'however'. ☐

When you're writing about a new person or subject. ☐

When you reach the end of the page. ☐

2 Draw a line to show whether each statement is **true** or **false**.

Paragraphs make your writing easier to read.

Paragraphs have to start with 'and'.

Paragraphs have to be two lines long.

A new paragraph starts on a new line.

Paragraphs are groups of sentences.

Only use paragraphs when you want to.

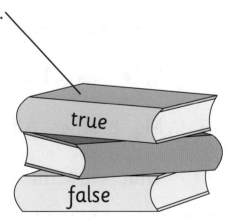

true

false

3 Write whether the sentences in each of the paragraphs below are linked by <u>time</u>, <u>person</u> or <u>subject</u>.

Emma is the most interesting person I know. She has bright red hair and always wears big pink glasses. She must be quite clever because she is always reading.

....

My favourite year at school was Year Two. When I was in Year Two I had lots of friends, and I found school really fun. I wish I was still in Year Two.

....

We have lost our cat. He didn't come in for his breakfast this morning, and I am very worried about him. His name is Ben and he has stripy ginger fur.

....

4 Put <u>three</u> paragraph markers (//) in the passage below to show where <u>new paragraphs</u> should <u>start</u>.

A few months ago, Amal's mum took her to visit the zoo. She saw lions and tigers, as well as monkeys and bears. Amal thought it was amazing. The next weekend Amal found out that the zoo wanted some school-children to start working there. She signed up straight away. Now Amal goes along to the zoo every Saturday morning. She feeds the animals and helps to look after them. Next month, Amal is going to be there when the new baby penguins are born. She can't wait!

5 <u>Draw lines</u> to match the sentences that belong in the <u>same paragraph</u>.

| Our family dog is called Rosie. | It was green with a yellow flower pattern. |

| Last year I got a dress for my birthday. | His older brother, George, has blue eyes. |

| Fred has ginger hair and brown eyes. | She is seven years old and loves to play catch. |

6 In <u>two</u> of these passages, a new paragraph starts in the <u>wrong place</u>. Put a <u>cross</u> next to these two passages.

Today we are going on a long drive to London. We're leaving early in the morning so I'm going to sleep in the car.
    I hope I don't feel travel sick. Next weekend, we have to stay at home because my brother has a football tournament.

☐

My dad is a vet. He has his own animal surgery in the centre of our town, and he looks after all sorts of animals.
    My mum is a police officer. Sometimes she lets me try on her hat and pretend to be a police officer as well!

☐

I am really good at drawing. I practise most days by drawing things around the house and in the garden.
    I can draw for hours until my picture's just right. I am also good at acting. On Fridays, I go to acting classes.

☐

....

Now Try This Look at the passages that you crossed in question 6. Where should the paragraph breaks go? Explain the reason for each one.

....

 ✓   ✓   ✓

Headings and Subheadings

Headings and subheadings make a text clearer and easier to read.
Headings tell the reader the main topic of the text.
Subheadings divide up the text into smaller sections.

1 Put a <u>tick</u> next to the statements that are <u>true</u>.

You should have a new heading for each point. ☐

A heading tells you the main subject of the text. ☐

You can only have one subheading per page. ☐

Subheadings break up a text into smaller sections. ☐

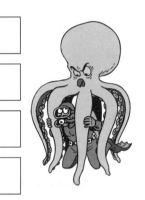

2 Draw lines to link each <u>subheading</u> to the correct section of <u>text</u>.

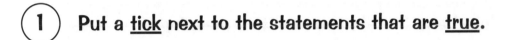
Headings and subheadings are usually found in non-fiction texts.

Traditional English Foods

<u>Fish and Chips</u>   <u>Sticky Toffee Pudding</u>   <u>English Breakfast</u>

Eggs, bacon, sausages, beans and toast. Often served all day — not just for breakfast.

Deep-fried fish served with chips. Usually served as take-away food with salt and vinegar.

A steamed pudding made with sponge, dates and toffee sauce. Often served with custard.

Now Try This

Write three short paragraphs about different things you have eaten this week. Give each paragraph a subheading.

Section 11 — Prefixes

Prefixes – 'un', 'dis' and 'mis'

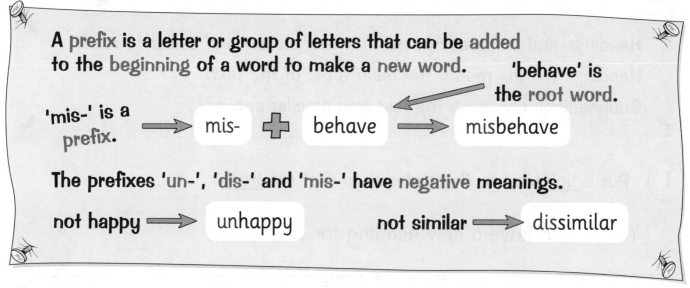

A prefix is a letter or group of letters that can be added to the beginning of a word to make a new word.

'behave' is the root word.

'mis-' is a prefix. ➞ mis- ➕ behave ➞ misbehave

The prefixes 'un-', 'dis-' and 'mis-' have negative meanings.

not happy ⟹ unhappy   not similar ⟹ dissimilar

---

1 Split the words below into <u>prefixes</u> and <u>root</u> words.

unknown ➡ .... ➕ ....

misprint ➡ .... ➕ ....

disapprove ➡ .... ➕ ....

uneven ➡ .... ➕ ....

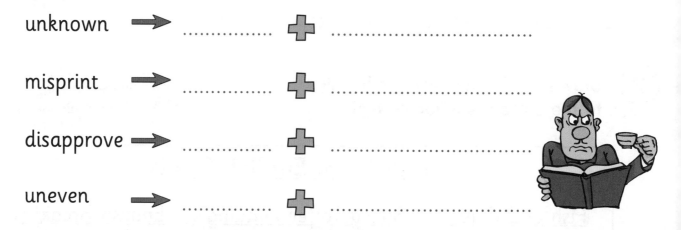

---

2 Add <u>un-</u>, <u>dis-</u> or <u>mis-</u> to spell the words below correctly. Then write the words out <u>in full</u>.

...........aware ➡ ....

...........equal ➡ ....

...........regard ➡ ....

...........paid ➡ ....

...........behave ➡ ....

3 Underline the words below that have the wrong <u>prefixes</u>.
Then write the <u>correct</u> spellings on the dotted lines.

unable

dislike

diskind

discalculate

unspell   misappoint

....

....

....

....

4 Draw lines from the <u>prefixes</u> to the correct <u>root</u> words.

dis-

mis-

own

miss

treat

please

match

agree

Write the <u>completed</u> words in the box.

5 Complete the words in these sentences using <u>un-</u>, <u>dis-</u> or <u>mis-</u>.

Asha went to hospital last night because she was very ....well.

Joanne left her car ....locked because the lock was broken.

The magician stepped inside the box and then ....appeared.

Pascal ....understood the question and got the answer wrong.

When we got to the hotel, we ....packed and ran to the pool.

Now Try This   Can you use each word from question 1 in a sentence?

Section 11 — Prefixes

Prefixes – 're' and 'anti'

The prefix 're-' means 'again' or 'back' when you add it to a root word.

reappear ⟵ 'reappear' means 'to appear again'

The prefix 'anti' means 'not' or 'against' when you add it to a root word.

'antisocial' means 'not sociable' ⟶ antisocial

1 Add **re-** or **anti-** to **finish** each word correctly.

...............clockwise   ....septic   ....charge

...............fresh   ....write   ....climax

...............create   ....heat   ....design

2 Draw lines from the **prefixes** to the correct **root** words.

Write the **completed** words in the box.

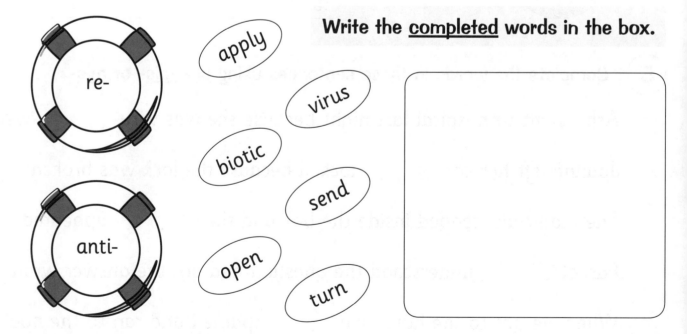

re-

anti-

apply

virus

biotic

send

open

turn

 "I built an enormous gingerbread house." How does the meaning of this sentence change when you add the prefix 're-' to the word 'built'?

Prefixes – 'sub' and 'super'

The prefix 'sub-' means 'under' when you add it to a root word.

subway ⬅ 'subway' means 'under the way'.

The prefix 'super' means 'above' or 'more than' when you add it to a root word.

'superstar' means 'a very successful person'. ➡ superstar

1 Circle the __correct__ spelling of each __noun__ to complete the sentences.

The <u>supermarine</u> / <u>submarine</u> can reach depths of 300 feet.

Rupert stuck his fingers together with <u>superglue</u> / <u>subglue</u>.

Eren hates going to the <u>supermarket</u> / <u>submarket</u> on Saturdays.

The brave <u>superhero</u> / <u>subhero</u> came to the city's rescue.

2 Complete the words in these sentences using <u>sub</u>- or <u>super</u>-.

My sandwich fell into the river and began to ....merge.

The train whizzed past at ....sonic speed.

The class was ....divided into three groups of ten people.

Lily didn't understand what each ....heading meant.

3 Write as many words as you can that start with each of these __prefixes__.

super-...

sub-...

Use as many words from question 3 as you can in a single sentence.

Section 12 — Suffixes and Word Endings

Suffixes – 'ing' and 'ed'

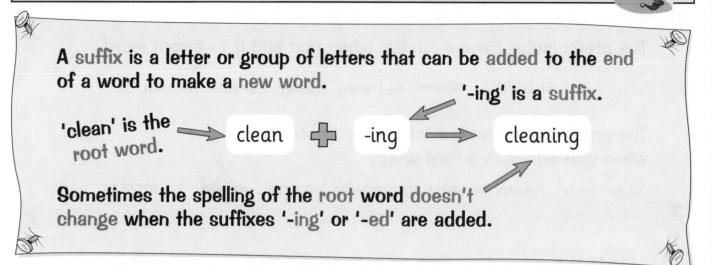

A **suffix** is a letter or group of letters that can be **added** to the end of a word to make a **new word**.

'-ing' is a **suffix**.

'clean' is the root word. → clean ➕ -ing → cleaning

Sometimes the spelling of the **root** word **doesn't change** when the suffixes '-ing' or '-ed' are added.

(1) Add the <u>suffixes</u> to the root words and then write the words out in <u>full</u>.

hunt- ➕ -ing / -ed ➡ ....

jump- ➕ -ing / -ed ➡ ....

treat- ➕ -ing / -ed ➡ ....

(2) Add -<u>ing</u> or -<u>ed</u> to the sentences below so that they make sense.

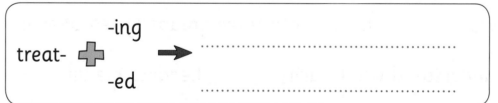

Ishra enjoys perform....... in plays at the theatre.

The clown entertain....... the children at the village fair.

The postman is deliver....... letters and parcels to Mr MacDonald.

Sometimes the spelling of the root word changes when the suffixes '-ing' or '-ed' are added.

The 'y' in 'marry' changes to 'i'.

marry ➕ -ed ➡️ married

(3) Circle the **correct** spelling of each word to complete the sentences.

Ben is out <u>shoping</u> / <u>shopping</u> with Nancy.

Sometimes a letter is <u>doubled</u> when '-ing' or '-ed' are added.

I am <u>struggleing</u> / <u>struggling</u> to do my homework.

Janice was <u>employed</u> / <u>emploied</u> by the local council.

My sister always <u>enjoyed</u> / <u>enjoied</u> playing rugby.

The men <u>carryed</u> / <u>carried</u> the furniture up five flights of stairs.

The roadblock has <u>stoped</u> / <u>stopped</u> the traffic in Ponty Lane.

On Tuesday, Laurence is <u>celebrateing</u> / <u>celebrating</u> his birthday.

(4) Underline the words that are spelt <u>incorrectly</u> below.
Then write the **correct** spellings out in full on the dotted lines.

worryed   smiling   ....

driving   balanceing

                                ....

puzzling   taking   ....

        hurryed

biting   cryed   ....

Now Try This   Write down three words that follow each of these rules when you add '-ing' or '-ed':   1) change 'y' to 'i'   2) remove an 'e'   3) double a letter

 ✓   ✓   ✓

Section 12 — Suffixes and Word Endings

Suffixes – 'er' and 'est'

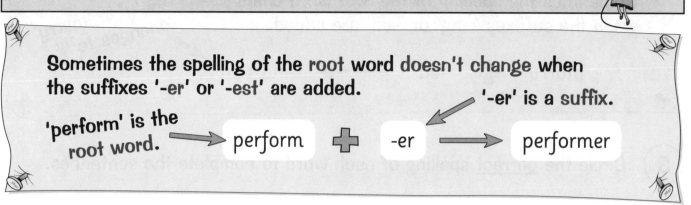

Sometimes the spelling of the root word doesn't change when the suffixes '-er' or '-est' are added.

'-er' is a suffix.

'perform' is the root word. → perform ➕ -er → performer

---

1 Add -er and -est to spell the words below correctly.

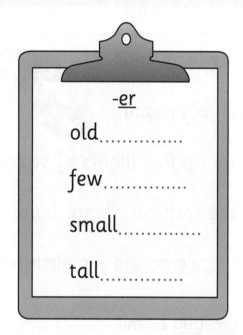

-er

old..............

few..............

small.............

tall..............

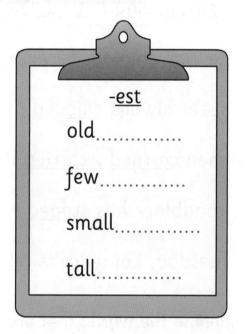

-est

old..............

few..............

small.............

tall..............

---

2 Add -er or -est to the sentences below so that they make sense.

Russia is cold...... than Iceland, but Antarctica is the cold....... place.

Carla is the fast...... runner at our athletics club.

Queen Lauren I is rich...... than King Michael II.

---

3 Add -er to spell the words below correctly.

sing..............   garden.............   teach..............

bank..............   plumb.............   wait..............

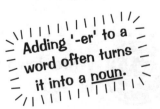

Adding '-er' to a word often turns it into a <u>noun</u>.

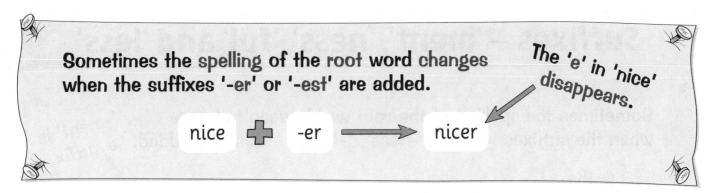

Sometimes the spelling of the root word changes when the suffixes '-er' or '-est' are added.

The 'e' in 'nice' disappears.

nice ➕ -er ➡️ nicer

4 Underline the word that is spelt <u>correctly</u> in each word pair below.

nastyer / nastier   voteer / voter   spicyer / spicier

tinyest / tiniest   danceer / dancer

buyer / buier   fater / fatter   easyest / easiest

5 Circle the words that are spelt <u>incorrectly</u> in the passage below.

Yesterday the funnyest thing happened. The manageer of our local supermarket spent hours making the floors of his shop shinyer than they had ever been before. But that afternoon a group of bikeers walked all over the shop in the muddyest boots I have ever seen.

Write the <u>correct</u> spellings in the box.

Now Try This — Write a sentence that has a word ending in '-er' and a word ending in '-est'.

Section 12 — Suffixes and Word Endings

Suffixes – 'ment', 'ness', 'ful' and 'less'

Sometimes the spelling of the root word doesn't change when the suffixes '-ment', '-ness', '-ful' or '-less' are added.

'-ment' is a suffix.

'agree' is the root word. → agree ✚ -ment → agreement

1 Draw lines from the word <u>beginnings</u> to the correct word <u>endings</u>.

fear-

stress-

sad-

enjoy-

play-

Write the <u>completed</u> words in the box.

-ment

-ness

-ful

2 Complete the sentences below using the <u>correct</u> words from the box.

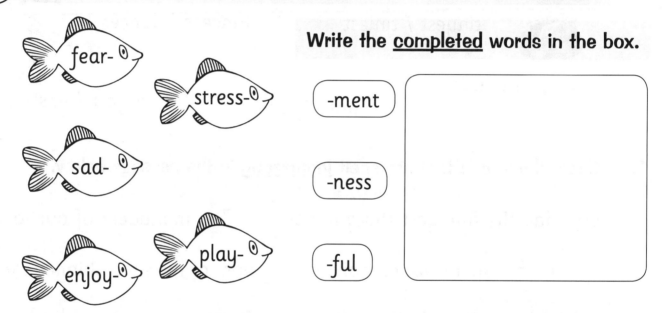

brightment / brightness   equipment / equipless

spotless / spotful

Shu cleaned the kitchen and now it looks ....

The scouts made sure they had the right ....

The seagulls were blinded by the .... of the sun.

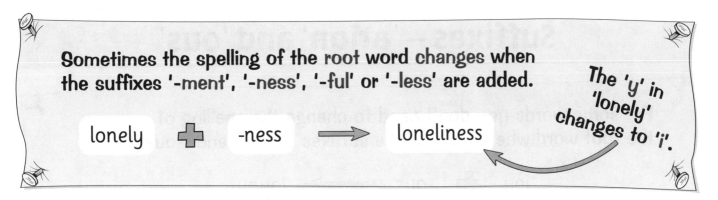

Sometimes the spelling of the root word changes when the suffixes '-ment', '-ness', '-ful' or '-less' are added.

lonely ➕ -ness ➡ loneliness

The 'y' in 'lonely' changes to 'i'.

3 Circle the <u>correct</u> spelling of each word to complete the sentences.

Lots of people think Italy is a <u>beautyful</u> / <u>beautiful</u> country.

I couldn't buy anything — I was <u>pennyless</u> / <u>penniless</u>.

It was <u>laziness</u> / <u>lazyness</u> that stopped me from doing his work.

We were surprised by the <u>bumpyness</u> / <u>bumpiness</u> of the road.

The king was <u>mercyful</u> / <u>merciful</u> and set the prisoner free.

Jessica's face beamed with <u>happyness</u> / <u>happiness</u>.

Faizal's eyes shone with <u>merryment</u> / <u>merriment</u>.

4 Draw lines from the words on the left to the <u>correct</u> words on the right.

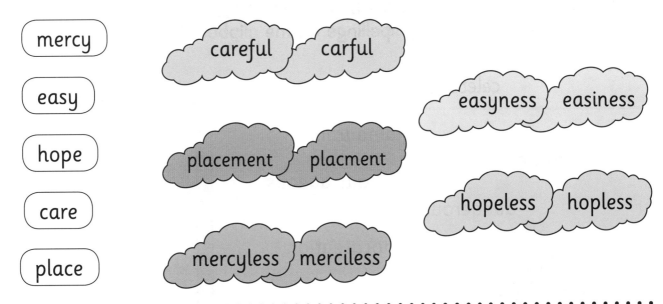

mercy

easy

hope

care

place

careful / carful

easyness / easiness

placement / placment

hopeless / hopless

mercyless / merciless

Now Try This

Can you think of three root words that you can add both '-ful' and '-less' to?

Section 12 — Suffixes and Word Endings

Suffixes – 'ation' and 'ous'

For some words you **don't** need to change the **spelling** of the **root word** when you add the suffixes '-ation' and '-ous'.

joy ➕ -ous ➡️ joyous

Sometimes the **spelling** of the **root** word changes when you add '-ation' or '-ous'.

The 'u' in 'humour' disappears.

humour ➕ -ous ➡️ humorous

1 Add either **-ation** or **-ous** to spell the words below correctly.

plant ➕ -ation ➡️ ....

fame ➕ -ous ➡️ ....

public ➕ -ation ➡️ ....

2 Underline the words below that are spelt **incorrectly**. Then write the **correct** spellings on the clipboard.

celebrateion

glamourous

limitation

outrageous

dangerous

locateation

relaxation

Section 12 — Suffixes and Word Endings

3 Circle the **correct** spelling of each word to complete the sentences.

Kelsey was busy with the party <u>prepareation</u> / <u>preparation</u>.

We are sending Qudsia an <u>invitation</u> / <u>inviteation</u> to the party.

I think that going to school on a Sunday is <u>outragous</u> / <u>outrageous</u>.

4 Add -<u>ation</u> or -<u>ous</u> to the sentences below so that they make sense.

Snowdonia is a mountain.................. region in Wales.

Swimming in deep water can be danger.................. .

Ali was cross that Feng had given her the wrong inform.................. .

Driving in icy conditions can be hazard.................. .

The hotel did not live up to Mr Butler's expect.................. .

5 Use the <u>clues</u> to <u>work out</u> each word ending with -<u>ous</u>.

A funny joke is... ➡ | h | | l | | | | | |

| c | | | r | | g | | | s | ⬅ Heroes are usually...

Superstars are often very... ➡ | g | l | | m | | | | | |

| i | | f | | | | | | | ⬅ Some illnesses are...

Now Try This — The suffix '-ation' turns verbs into nouns. Can you work out which verb each of these '-ation' words comes from?   creation   education   vibration

 ☑   ☑   ☑   Section 12 — Suffixes and Word Endings

Suffixes – 'ly'

For some words you don't need to change the spelling of the root word when you add the suffix '-ly'.

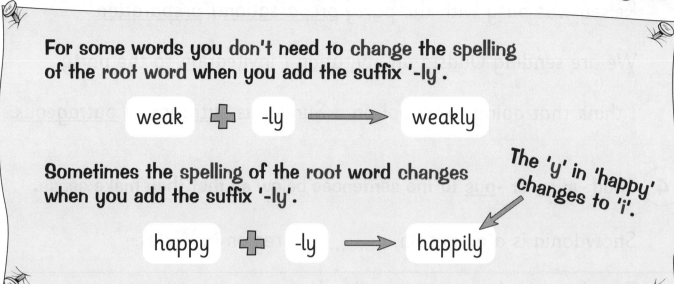

weak ➕ -ly ⟶ weakly

Sometimes the spelling of the root word changes when you add the suffix '-ly'.

happy ➕ -ly ⟶ happily

The 'y' in 'happy' changes to 'i'.

① **Add -ly to spell the words below correctly.**

angry ➕ -ly ⟶ ....

rude ➕ -ly ⟶ ....

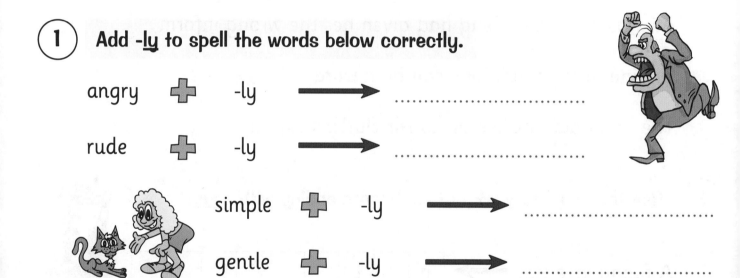

simple ➕ -ly ⟶ ....

gentle ➕ -ly ⟶ ....

② **Circle the correct spelling of each word to complete the sentences.**

At the zoo, Mikey saw a deadly / deadily spider.

The secretary busyly / busily sorted through the post.

Mrs Fredrickson franticly / frantically searched for her car keys.

Sanjay gladly / gladily received the present from Greg.

The Queen sat nobley / nobly on her throne.

3 Put a <u>tick</u> in the boxes next to the words that are spelt <u>correctly</u>.
Put a <u>cross</u> in the boxes next to the words that are spelt <u>incorrectly</u>.

cuddlely ☐   boldly ☐   sensiblely ☐

badly ☐   softly ☐   calmly ☐

humblely ☐   subtlely ☐   meanly ☐

Write the <u>correct</u> spellings of the words you put a cross next to below.

☐

4 Complete the sentences below using the <u>correct</u> words from the box.

ably / ablely   warmly / warmily   slightely / slightly

Mr Matthews .... welcomed his guests.

Paul was .... worried that Don was lost.

Pam .... completed the crossword.

5 Write as many words as you can that end in <u>-ly</u> on the lines below.

....

....

Now Try This — Write a short paragraph about how you get ready for school.
Use as many words ending in '-ly' as you can.

Section 12 — Suffixes and Word Endings

Word Endings – 'sure' and 'ture'

The endings '-sure' and '-ture' sound similar, but are spelt differently.

enclosure   picture

1   Draw lines from the word <u>beginnings</u> to the correct word <u>endings</u>.

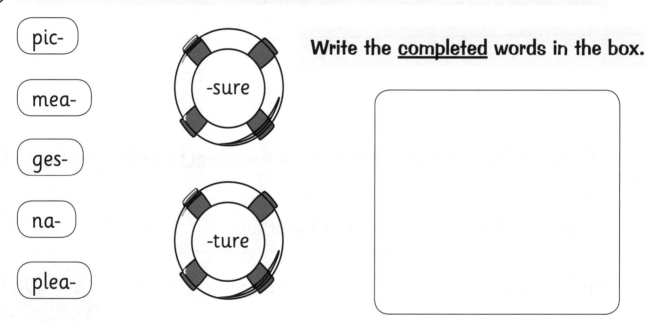

pic-

mea-

ges-

na-

plea-

-sure

-ture

Write the <u>completed</u> words in the box.

2   Circle the <u>correct</u> spelling of each word to complete the sentences.

Anne thinks the <u>enclosure</u> / <u>encloture</u> is too small for the animals.

Kevin's company has started to <u>manufacsure</u> / <u>manufacture</u> fridges.

Despite the argument, I managed to keep my <u>composure</u> / <u>compoture</u>.

The witch cooked up a <u>mixsure</u> / <u>mixture</u> of slugs and snails.

The architect said the <u>structure</u> / <u>strucsure</u> was secure.

Purple Beard is searching for his lost, buried <u>treasure</u> / <u>treature</u>.

3 Add either -<u>sure</u> or -<u>ture</u> to spell the words below correctly.

lei- ➕ .... ➡ ....

tor- ➕ .... ➡ ....

crea- ➕ .... ➡ ....

4 Sort the groups of letters below into the <u>right order</u> to spell a word ending in -<u>sure</u> or -<u>ture</u>.

sure   ea   tr ➡ ....

.... ⬅ ni   ture   fur

tem   a   per   ture ➡ ....

.... ⬅ po   com   sure

ture   ven   ad ➡ ....

5 Write as many words as you can that end in -<u>sure</u> or -<u>ture</u> on the dotted lines below.

....

....

....

Use each word from question 4 in a different sentence.

Section 12 — Suffixes and Word Endings

Section 13 — Confusing Words

The Short 'i' Sound

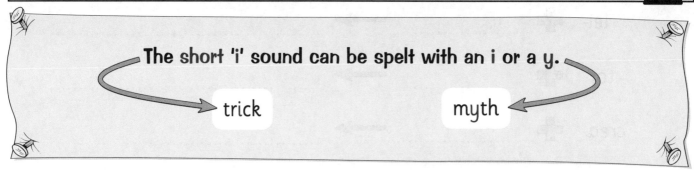

The short 'i' sound can be spelt with an i or a y.

trick   myth

1 <u>Draw lines</u> to show which of the words below have a <u>short</u> 'i' sound and which have a <u>long</u> 'i' sound.

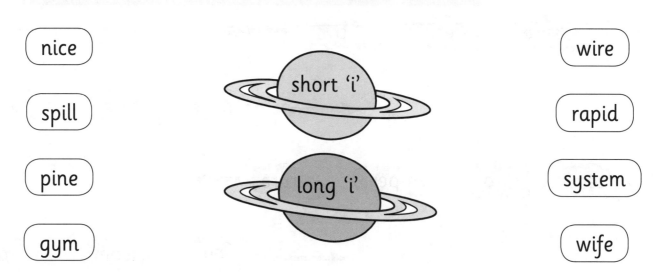

nice

spill

pine

gym

short 'i'

long 'i'

wire

rapid

system

wife

2 <u>Circle</u> the words that are spelt <u>correctly</u>.

wish / wysh   tyger / tiger   chin / chyn

tyme / time   cript / crypt

3 Fill in the <u>missing letter</u> in each word.

.....nsect   pan.....c   g.....ft   cr.....stal

s.....rup   m.....stery   sat.....sfy   s.....nce

Now Try This List as many words containing the short 'i' sound as you can in two minutes.

Section 13 — Confusing Words

The Hard 'c' Sound

The hard 'c' sound is like a 'k' sound.
Here are a few ways it can be spelt:

prickly   king   picnic

1 The hard 'c' sounds in the words below are missing.
Draw lines to match each word to its missing part.

atta?   'ck'   ?itten

wal?ing   'k'   cri?et

?offee   'c'   do?tor

2 Use the picture clues to correctly spell the hard 'c' words below.

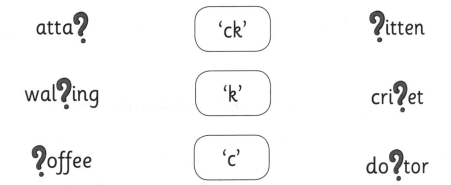

3 Use c, k or ck to complete the hard 'c' words in these sentences.

I often get homesi.... when I am away for a long time.

The o....topus has eight tentacles.

There are 206 bones in an adult human s....eleton.

 Write a short passage about a football match.
Include each spelling of the hard 'c' sound at least once.

Section 13 — Confusing Words

The Soft 'c' Sound

In some words, the letter c makes the soft 'c' sound. This is like an 's' sound. → | cinema | place |

1 <u>Underline</u> the words that contain a <u>soft 'c'</u> sound.

sentence   space   crane   excited

magic   October   pencil   create

2 <u>Circle</u> the words below that are spelt <u>correctly</u>.

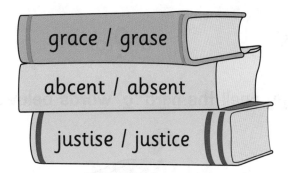

grace / grase

abcent / absent

justise / justice

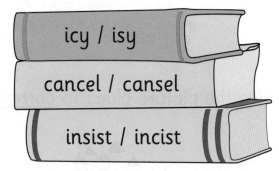

icy / isy

cancel / cansel

insist / incist

3 Use <u>s</u> or <u>c</u> to fill in the gaps in these words.

| s | e | n | | e | |

| a | | i | d |

| d | a | n | | e |

| s | p | i | | y |

| d | e | | e | n | t |

| h | o | u | | e |

| c | h | a | | e |

| u | p | | e | t |

 Write sentences using each of the correctly spelt words in question 2.

The 'sh' Sound

The 'sh' sound can be spelt in several different ways.

| share | sure | chef | mission |

1 Use the picture clues to <u>correctly</u> spell the '<u>sh</u>' sound words below.

......oe   para......ute   ......ugar   ......ark

2 <u>Circle</u> the <u>correct</u> spelling of each word to complete the sentences.

Jenny put her dirty clothes in the washing <u>machine</u> / <u>mashine</u>.

Amar sneezed into his <u>tissue</u> / <u>tisue</u>.

I need to buy more <u>champoo</u> / <u>shampoo</u>.

Check if it says anything about it in the <u>broshure</u> / <u>brochure</u>.

3 <u>Complete</u> the sentences below using the <u>correct</u> words from the box.

> achamed / ashamed   pressure / preshure

I'm .... to say that I don't know the answer.

The .... was building as the questions got harder.

 Now Try This Write down four words that contain different spellings of the 'sh' sound. Try to use words that aren't on this page.

Section 13 — Confusing Words

The 'ay' Sound

The 'ay' sound can be spelt in different ways.

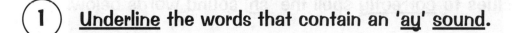

mail   display   frame

(1) <u>Underline</u> the words that contain an '<u>ay</u>' <u>sound</u>.

Try saying the words out loud to help you answer this question.

afraid   canal   brave

anyway   stare   essay   water

(2) Write the <u>correct</u> spelling of each word on the dotted lines.

 saylor   graypes   calculaite

....

(3) <u>Find</u> the words with '<u>ay</u>' sounds in the wordsearch.

translate	faint
plane	waist
bake	clay
behave	Monday
paid	always
nail	dismay

```
T M O N D A Y E E
H R B A K E F D A
P L A N E N A I L
A A E N R T I S W
I C R I S S N M A
D L R D E L T A Y
W A I S T S A Y S
E Y N C E B P T E
B E H A V E E R E
```

 Now Try This Write three sentences, using as many words from question 3 as you can.

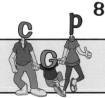

Word Families

Word families are groups of words that contain the
same root. Their meanings are related — like a family.

All of these words contain
the root 'act'. They are all
about doing something.

 | action | active | react |

1 **Underline** the words that belong to the same <u>word family</u> as <u>frost</u>.

frosting   lost   decline   frostbite

define   frosted   defrost   bitten

2 Draw lines to <u>match</u> each word to the box
that contains a word from the <u>same family</u>.

deface   face   trustworthy

distrust   movement

                        move

preface   facing

                        trust

remove   trusted

3 Write two more words for each of the <u>word families</u> below.

take / mistake ➡ ....

date / dating ➡ ....

do / redo ➡ ....

 Think of four words that belong to the same family as each
of these words: 1) luck   2) play   3) form

Section 13 — Confusing Words

Plurals

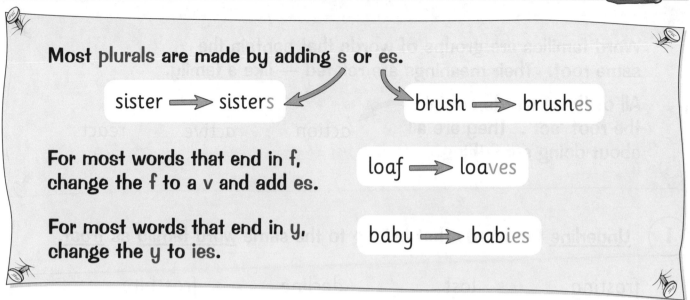

Most plurals are made by adding s or es.

sister ⟶ sisters   brush ⟶ brushes

For most words that end in f, change the f to a v and add es.

loaf ⟶ loaves

For most words that end in y, change the y to ies.

baby ⟶ babies

1 Add <u>s</u> or <u>es</u> to each of these words to make them plural.

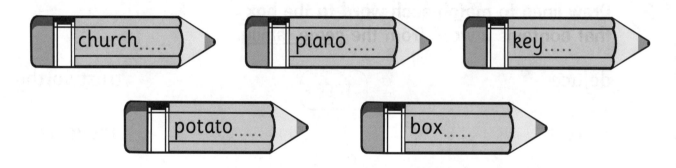

church.....

piano.....

key.....

potato.....

box.....

2 These plurals are spelt <u>incorrectly</u>. Write the <u>correct spelling</u> of each.

ponys ⟶ ....   wolfs ⟶ ....

leafes ⟶ ....   thiefs ⟶ ....

difficultys ⟶ ....   apologys ⟶ ....

shopes ⟶ ....   shelfs ⟶ ....

torchs ⟶ ....   foxs ⟶ ....

bucketes ⟶ ....   penciles ⟶ ....

Some plurals don't follow the rules. You just have to learn these.

sheep ⟹ sheep   foot ⟹ feet   child ⟹ children

3 **Complete** the table below.

Word	Plural
goose	....
mouse	....
reflex	....
elf	....
woman	....

4 **Finish** these sentences by writing the plural of the words in brackets.

I always clean my .... (tooth) before bed.

My aunt split the cake into two .... (half).

The rock climbers saw the .... (cliff) as a challenge.

5 **Write** the plural of each of these words in a sentence.

donkey ⟹ ....

sandwich ⟹ ....

batch ⟹ ....

Can you write a sentence that includes plurals ending in 's', 'es' and 'ies'?

Possessive Apostrophes

Possessive apostrophes show that something belongs to someone.

Jim's dogs ⟶ The dogs belonging to Jim.

You don't need an apostrophe to show that a word is plural.

1 Cross the phrases which use apostrophes <u>incorrectly</u>.

Adjoa's dad ☐   Peter's kitten's ☐   Gemmas' bat ☐

Elsa's shoes ☐   Jeremys' pens ☐   Adrian's ball ☐

Rewrite the <u>incorrect</u> phrases with <u>apostrophes</u> in the <u>correct</u> places.

2 <u>Underline</u> the words in the passage that are <u>missing</u> apostrophes. Then <u>rewrite</u> the words with the <u>correct apostrophes</u>.

Dear Sura,

Please come to Judiths party tomorrow.

We are going in Mums car. She is taking me

and Matts sister, so there will definitely be

room for you and Jackies cake. Bring Kevins

playing cards as well.

....

....

....

....

....

'It's' is a shortened form of 'it is' or 'it has'.

It's raining $\longrightarrow$ It is raining.

The word 'its' means 'belonging to it'.

Its paw $\longrightarrow$ The paw belonging to it.

The word 'its' never has a possessive apostrophe.

3 Use either <u>its</u> or <u>it's</u> to <u>complete</u> the sentences below.

.... your turn to do the washing-up.

The gorilla beat .... chest to scare .... rival.

Mr Chen's cat ate all of .... food straight away.

4 <u>Rewrite</u> the phrases below using a <u>possessive apostrophe</u>.

The rabbit belonging to my sister $\longrightarrow$ .... My sister's rabbit ....

The ship belonging to the pirate $\longrightarrow$ ....

The mop belonging to the cleaner $\longrightarrow$ ....

5 <u>Write</u> sentences using <u>possessive apostrophes</u> with each of the words below.

grandma $\longrightarrow$ ....

Thomas $\longrightarrow$ ....

parrot $\longrightarrow$ ....

Now Try This — Find five objects that belong to different people. Write a list of the objects, using possessive apostrophes to show who they belong to.

Homophones

Homophones are words that sound the same, but have different meanings and spellings.

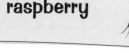

bury

To bury something is to cover it completely.

berry

A berry is a small fruit. E.g. raspberry

(1) Write the <u>homophone</u> that matches each picture.

main ➡ ....

be ➡ ....

bare ➡ ....

son ➡ ....

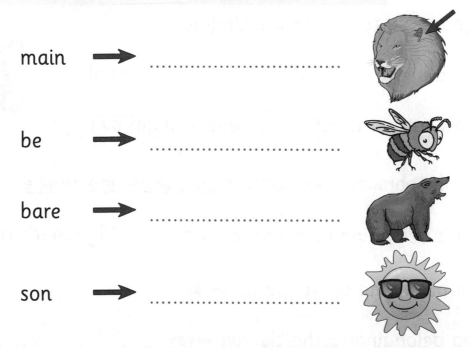

(2) Circle the <u>correct</u> spelling of each word to <u>complete</u> the sentences.

Vegetarians don't eat <u>meet</u> / <u>meat</u>.

Where shall we <u>meat</u> / <u>meet</u>?

I can't <u>accept</u> / <u>except</u> this.

I like all vegetables <u>accept</u> / <u>except</u> carrots.

Don't <u>brake</u> / <u>break</u> anything.

Make sure you <u>brake</u> / <u>break</u> at the corner.

3 Fill in the <u>gaps</u> in these sentences using the <u>correct</u> words from the box.

> there   their   they're

Becky and Habiba dyed .... hair the same colour.

Are .... any biscuits left in the tin?

Three people said .... coming to my party.

4 Find a <u>homophone</u> for each of the words below.
Then find <u>all</u> of the words in the wordsearch.

sea ➡ | s | e | e |

reign ➡ | r | a | | |

here ➡ | h | | a | |

dear ➡ | d | | | r |

maid ➡ | m | | | e |

```
O  W  E  R  D  E  E  R
R  B  A  E  E  W  D  A
L  M  A  I  D  L  I  L
A  E  O  G  T  N  S  W
D  R  H  N  S  S  E  E
E  H  E  R  E  T  A  Y
A  M  A  D  E  R  Y  S
R  N  R  A  I  N  T  E
```

5 Write each of these <u>words</u> in a <u>sentence</u>.

to ➡ ....

two ➡ ....

too ➡ ....

Now Try This Can you write a sentence that uses all of the homophones in question 3?

Section 13 — Confusing Words

Mixed Spelling Practice

1 Split the words below into <u>prefixes</u> and <u>root</u> words.

unpaid ➡ .... ✚ ....

subcategory ➡ .... ✚ ....

mistrust ➡ .... ✚ ....

recycle ➡ .... ✚ ....

2 Add the <u>suffixes</u> to the words below and then write the words out in <u>full</u>.

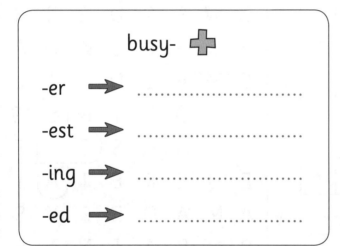

busy- ✚

-er ➡ ....

-est ➡ ....

-ing ➡ ....

-ed ➡ ....

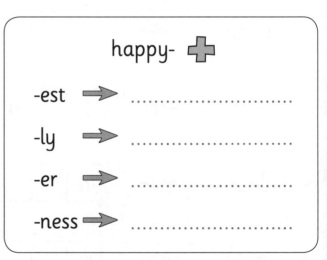

happy- ✚

-est ➡ ....

-ly ➡ ....

-er ➡ ....

-ness ➡ ....

3 Circle the words that are spelt <u>incorrectly</u>.
Write the <u>correct</u> spellings on the dotted lines.

antisocial   submarine   information

merryment   usualy   disimilar

angryly   picsure   superglue

....

....

....

....

4 The <u>hard</u> '<u>c</u>' sound in each word below is missing.
Draw lines to <u>match</u> each word to its missing part.

ba**?**   **'ck'**   tal**?**

loo**?**   **'k'**   **?**ook

s**?**etch   **'c'**   ro**?**et

5 Circle the <u>correct</u> spelling of each word to <u>complete</u> the sentences.

The detective promised to look into the <u>mistery</u> / <u>mystery</u>.

When we go skiing, we stay in a <u>shalet</u> / <u>chalet</u>.

I can't lift that <u>weight</u> / <u>waight</u>.

Tim needed to find a cash <u>machine</u> / <u>mashine</u>.

<u>Thay</u> / <u>They</u> are going on holiday next month.

The <u>mith</u> / <u>myth</u> was fascinating to learn about.

6 <u>Complete</u> the <u>table</u> below.

Word	Plural
country	....
box	....
thief	....
potato	....

7 **Cross the phrases which use apostrophes <u>incorrectly</u>.**

Andys' hat ☐   Ayse's mum ☐   Ruths' mug ☐

Lily's cat's ☐   Taran's pencil ☐   Sam's dogs ☐

8 **Solve the <u>clues</u> to complete the crossword.**

<u>Across</u>

1. Connects your head to your shoulders.

2. To behave badly.

3. One less than twice.

4. Magicians perform these.

<u>Down</u>

1. The person who lives next door.

2. A tunnel under a road.

9 **Write each <u>pair of homophones</u> in a <u>sentence</u>.**

sail / sale ➡ ....

....

I / eye ➡ ....

....

Glossary

Adjective — A word that describes a noun, e.g. **spicy** curry.

Adverb — A word that describes a verb, e.g. end **abruptly**.

Article — The words **a**, **an** and **the**.

Clause — Part of a sentence that contains a **subject** (**someone** or **something** doing the action) and a **verb**.

Command — A sentence that gives an **instruction** or an **order**.

Conjunction — A word or phrase that **joins** two parts of a sentence.

Exclamation — A sentence that shows **strong feelings**, beginning with 'how' or 'what'.

Main clause — A clause that **makes sense** on its own, e.g. <u>I like football</u> because it is fun.

Noun — A word that **names** something, e.g. **cat**, **James**, **Monday**.

Phrase — A group of words usually without a **verb**.

Preposition — Introduces a **pronoun**, **noun** or **noun phrase** and tells you **where**, **when** or **why** something happens.

Statement — A sentence that **tells** you something.

Subordinate clause — A clause that **doesn't make sense** on its own, e.g. I like football <u>because it is fun</u>.

Verb — A doing or being word, e.g. **run**, **appear**, **shout**, **be**.

Glossary

COMMON PUNCTUATION MARKS

Apostrophes — show **missing letters** and **possession**. | **'**

Capital letters — used for **starting** sentences and for **names** or **I**. | **A**

Commas — used to separate items in a **list**. | **,**

Exclamation marks — show **strong emotions** or **commands**. | **!**

Full stops — show where **sentences end**. | **.**

Inverted commas — show **direct speech**. They can also be called '**speech marks**'. | **" "**

Question marks — used at the **end** of **questions**. | **?**

USEFUL WORDS

Direct speech — The **actual words** the speaker says.

Heading — A description of the **main topic** of the text.

Paragraph — Used to **group** related sentences **together**.

Reported speech — A **description** of someone's speech.

Subheading — Smaller headings used to **split up** a text.

Answers

Grammar

Section 1 – Word Types

Page 4 – Nouns

1. You should have underlined: **Brazil**, **monkey**, **girl**, **pencil**, **April**, **Emma**.
2. Common nouns: **game**, **tree**, **dog**, **money**, **house**, **book**
   Proper nouns: **London**, **Daniel**, **December**, **Tuesday**, **Rachel**, **America**

Page 5 – Adjectives

1. You should have underlined: **happy**, **quiet**, **purple**, **small**, **famous**, **clever**, **silly**.
2. Any suitable adjectives. Examples:
   the **confused** bear, the **brown** bear
   the **happy** girl, the **relaxed** girl
   the **scared** penguin, the **running** penguin
   the **huge** carrot, the **big** carrot

Pages 6 and 7 – Articles

1. I would like **a** hamburger.
   Yesterday, we saw **an** alligator.
   Melanie has **a** TV in her room.
   Here's **an** apple.
2. There's **an** orange in the fruit bowl.
   My sister has got **a** boyfriend.
   A cat has just run through the garden.
   If it snows, we could build **an** igloo.
3. Olga saw **an** elephant on the way to school.
   There was **a** spider in the bath.
   The play was **a** disaster.
   An eagle flew over the houses.
4. We went to a café and Thomas ordered **a** drink.
   I would really like to go on **the** London Eye.
   Matthias and Isabel had **a** great time in Italy.
   He would like to know **the** truth.
   Mark says this book is **the** best one he's ever read.
   Jafar really needs **a** good night's sleep.
   The view from our bedroom window is wonderful.
5. When it's hot, we go out for **an** ice cream.
   Mum makes the best pancakes in **the** world.
   My computer has broken, so I need **a** new one.
   An afternoon walk through the park is a lovely idea.
   Harriet was excited about her trip to **the** Eiffel Tower.

Pages 8 and 9 – Verbs

1. You should have circled: **eat**, **be**, **see**, **talk**, **write**, **run**, **sit**.
2. He **has** a motorbike, a car and a van.
   I **do** my homework as soon as I **get** home.
   Jenny and Tariq **go** to the cinema on Fridays.
   Susie often **flies** to Germany to **see** her friends.
   The supporters **are** happy with the referee's decision.
3. Suma **enjoys** playing tennis at the weekend.
   The children **walk** to school every day.
   Craig and Will **take** the train to work.
   She **hates** doing the washing-up.
   Khalid usually **meets** his friends in the park.
4. Ronnie **annoys** his sister by pulling her hair.
   Our dog **chases** the cat around the garden.
   A ghost **lives** in the castle.
   Mum and Dad **prepare** the dinner.
5. **play**, **cut**

Pages 10 and 11 – Adverbs

1. You should have underlined: **always**, **slowly**, **gently**, **next**, **then**.
2. The guests will arrive **soon**.
   The dog **playfully** licked my nose.
   He **rarely** goes to London.
   The children **greedily** ate the chocolate.
   Ivy **always** drives Mike to the shops.
   Maya **accidentally** fell and grazed her arm.
3. It's our turn **next**.
   Jonathan doesn't **often** complain.
   Kenzo **quickly** ran to the door.
   Shops are **usually** open every Monday.
   Calvin **quietly** sneaked past the house.
   We **busily** sorted through our things.
   Violet is **normally** late for school.
   The pupil **rudely** interrupted the teacher.
4. I wish it was always open, but **sometimes** it's closed.
   We never run out — our milk is delivered **daily**.
   Gary ate a lot — **afterwards** he felt really full.
   There wasn't room inside, so I had to wait **outside**.
   My brother's lazy — he **never** helps us.
   Habiba **carefully** wrapped the presents.

Answers

Section 2 – Clauses and Phrases

Pages 12 and 13 – Clauses

1. Main clauses: **I love chips, they told lies, he plays hockey, it's dark, she's happy now**
   Subordinate clauses: **until they arrive, when it's over, while eating cheese, if you're coming, before the bell rang**

2. Li drives to work <u>when it rains</u>.
   The girls keep the light on <u>because they're afraid of the dark</u>.
   <u>After she had played tennis</u>, Jean went out for dinner.
   <u>If the water rises any further</u>, we'll have to get help.

3. You should have ticked:
   Before we go out to play, <u>we need to tidy up</u>.
   <u>The children were soaking wet</u> because it was raining.
   <u>We couldn't see the stars</u> until the sun had gone down.

4. He enjoys watching cartoons while eating popcorn.
   I had a pudding after my main meal.
   Jane will play tennis if it stops raining.
   Aasir can't go to school until he's feeling better.
   The musicians practised before the concert.

5. Any suitable main clauses.
   Examples:
   Before we had dinner, **we played a game of cards**.
   While Ishan plays the piano, **Charlie sings along**.
   When Mum arrived, **we all hid under the bed**.

Page 14 – Phrases

1. You should have ticked: **far too early, very difficult, really funny, before midnight**.

2. Any suitable phrases.
   Examples:
   Ava jumped **on the trampoline**.
   The teacher spoke **to the pupils**.
   Rabbits are **popular pets**.

Page 15 – Noun Phrases

1. You should have circled: **blue shoes, cuddly hamsters, those amazing colours, chocolate muffins, lazy elephants, all of the teachers**.
   The nouns are: **shoes, hamsters, colours, muffins, elephants, teachers**.

2. You should have circled: **monster, sofa, socks, houses**.

Pages 16 and 17 – Mixed Sentence Practice

1. Clauses: **let's go for a bike ride, sandwiches are nice, I like reading.**
   Phrases: **up the mountain, really tall men with red hair, a fun game.**

2. You should have circled: **every Wednesday, the deep, blue sea, a very muddy path.**

3. her shiny new bike: **noun phrase**
   After the sun had set: **subordinate clause**
   the deep, dark woods: **noun phrase**
   I cut the whole loaf of bread in half: **main clause**
   a small plate: **noun phrase**

4. Any suitable answers.
   Examples:
   I enjoyed playing football today **because we won the match**.
   He saw **the big pink teddy bear**, but he didn't like it.
   Time passes very quickly when you're having fun.

Section 3 – Sentences

Page 18 – Statements and Questions

1. Why is he angry? — question
   What's the time? — question
   I work in a bakery. — statement
   I am so hungry. — statement
   It is a windy day. — statement
   How old are you? — question
   When will you be back? — question
   My mum's name is Kathy. — statement

2. Are they ill?
   Are you fast?
   Am I outside?
   Is he alright?
   Are we downstairs?

Page 19 – Commands and Exclamations

1. Finish your vegetables. — C
   What a huge whale that was! — E
   How terrible that cake was! — E
   What a brilliant play we saw! — E
   How funny you are! — E
   What a day I've had! — E
   Fasten your seatbelts. — C
   How clever she is! — E
   Fill the pan with water. — C
   Share your sweets. — C

2. Commands:
   Hold the tray.
   Stop the car.
   Exclamations:
   What a thrill this is!
   How nice he is!

Section 4 – Conjunctions and Prepositions

Pages 20 and 21 – Conjunctions with Main Clauses

1. You should have circled: **so, nor, but, or, for, yet,** and

2. You should have underlined these words:
   I want to play outside <u>but</u> it's raining.
   Leo is going on holiday, <u>so</u> he needs to pack his suitcase.
   We visited Grandad <u>and</u> we gave him his birthday present.
   Tomek doesn't like sausages, <u>nor</u> does he like mashed potato.
   Daisy can't bake cakes, <u>yet</u> she can bake very good biscuits.
   Mr Davies is flying to France, <u>for</u> it's quicker than driving.

3. I want to play chess, **and** Rosie wants to play too.
   The zoo was closed, **so** (or **but**) we went to the museum.
   They can have ice cream **or** (or **and**) they can have fruit salad.
   The fields were flooded, **for** it had rained a lot.
   I don't like tomatoes, **but** I do like tomato ketchup.

4. I was late, **so** I ran to school.
   I can't play the piano, **but** I can play the flute.
   We could go out, **or** we could stay in.
   Aanya can ride a bike, **and** she can ride a horse.

Pages 22 and 23 – Conjunctions with Subordinate Clauses

1. You should have underlined these words:
   <u>Before</u> we go to America, we need to get some dollars.
   I think we should play tennis <u>if</u> the wind calms down.
   Lily crossed things off the list <u>as</u> her mum did the shopping.
   <u>After</u> she finished her main course, Leah ordered a dessert.

2. You should have circled: **because, when, Before, although, If**

3. I whisked the eggs **because** I needed them for my cake.
   Let's get some petrol **before** we completely run out.
   We had to unpack **after** we came back from camp.
   I wouldn't eat a worm **even if** you paid me to do it.
   I'm good at maths **while** Drew is better at English.

4. Any suitable endings.
   Examples:
   We usually play outside because **it's nice to get some fresh air**.
   Colin never feels very well after **eating too much**.
   Mum and Dad were pleased when **the plumber came**.
   The football match will be cancelled if **the pitch is too wet**.

Pages 24 and 25 – Prepositions

1. You should have circled: **under, into, in, on, over, to, above.**

2. The cat is **on** the bed.
   The bag is **next to** (or **beside** or **by**) the bed.
   The shoes are **under** (or **beneath**) the bed.
   The boy is sitting **at** the table.
   The lamp is **on** the table.
   The mouse is **under** (or **beneath**) the table.

3. Mrs Gibson burst **into** the classroom. — **where**
   I brush my teeth **before** bedtime. — **when**
   A mouse ran **past** my foot. — **where**
   Grandpa fell asleep **during** the film. — **when**
   They stayed in **because of** the storm. — **why**

4. The Channel Tunnel goes **under** the sea.
   It's a long journey **to** Scotland from London.
   It was too late to get the train home **after** the show.
   I will meet you at the gate **in** 10 minutes time.
   Tom's toucan flew **out of** the window and into the garden.

5. Any sentence that uses a preposition correctly.
   Example:
   The squirrel jumped **over the fallen tree.**

Answers

Section 5 – Verb Tenses

Pages 26 and 27 – Present Tense and Past Tense

1. Simple past: stayed, stared, told, bought, spoke, played
   Simple present: go, relax, run, jump, are

2.

Simple Present	Simple Past	Simple Present	Simple Past
I behave	I behaved	I talk	I talked
I offer	I offered	I enjoy	I enjoyed
I work	I worked	I need	I needed
I ask	I asked	I live	I lived
I hope	I hoped	I open	I opened

3. Akari visited me.
   We tore it up.
   Alisha talked a lot.
   Jenny fell over.
   Ben packed his bag.
   I took the register.

4. Across: 1: broke
           2: ate
           3: threw
           4: read
           5: danced
   Down: 1: beat
           2: froze
           3: wore
           4: dried

Pages 28 and 29 – Using 'ing' verbs in the Present

1. You should have ticked these sentences and underlined these words:
   The cat is sleeping on the rug.
   The church bells are ringing.
   Mrs Taylor is speaking to Miss Jones.

2. The children **are** laugh**ing** at Mr Burgess.
   My dad **is** pretend**ing** he's forgotten Mum's birthday.
   Janice **is** watch**ing** the pop band 'Give This' in concert.
   They **are** walk**ing** from Land's End to John o' Groats.
   Hasan and Scott **are** show**ing** Lisa around the town.

3. My sister is **racing** around the track.
   I am **leaving** the party at 8 o'clock.
   Jason's popcorn is **popping** in the pan.
   Dad is **taking** our dog for a walk.
   We are **trying** to find our way home.
   My aunt is **mopping** the kitchen floor.

4. A bird is tapping at the window.
   We are driving to Cardiff.
   I am inviting friends to my party.

Page 30 – Using 'ing' verbs in the Past

1. Harry **was playing** tennis outside.
   They **were making** paper planes.
   I **was dropping** Kyle off at home.
   She **was cleaning** her bedroom.
   We **were listening** to music.

2. I was helping Jake.
   Nawaz and Zara were chasing Marcus.
   We were putting up pictures.

Pages 31 to 33 – The Present Perfect

1. You should have underlined these sentences:
   Jim has followed me.
   She has arrived.
   I have scratched my glasses.
   Efua has explained it.
   Sue has talked to Phil.

2. Radhika has arranged the furniture.
   I have finished my homework.
   Somsak has married Victoria.
   We have painted the walls.

3. You should have circled these words:
   forgotten
   come
   stolen
   drunk
   risen

4. The wolf **has blown** the house down.
   Bob **has thanked** everyone.
   We **have shown** them our idea.
   My sister **has given** me her clothes.
   They **have kept** the money safe.
   We **have enjoyed** the holiday.
   I **have broken** my new game.
   The boys **have cheated** at cards.

5. I took / I have taken
   I hid / I have hidden
   I grew / I have grown

Answers

6. You should have ticked these sentences:
   Rosa has been to the zoo.
   Miles has done lots today.
   I have been outside.
   We have seen her.
   Helen has come too.
   Corrected sentences:
   The boys have seen Darren's car.
   I have come to visit you.
   Izzy has done the dishes.

Pages 34 and 35 – Staying in the Same Tense

1. You should have circled these words:
   take
   bought
   have
   baked
   pretend

2. You should have ticked these sentences:
   Last month I bought a book and I finished it in one day.
   I keep my room tidy but my twin leaves stuff everywhere.
   I rushed to school this morning and forgot my sports kit.

3. I quickly **licked** my lolly before it dripped onto the floor.
   Niall was being rude so Mrs Simon **made** him stay behind.
   I spend time with my sister and we **listen** to music.
   We watched a sad film at the weekend and my mum **cried**.

4. You should have circled and corrected these words:
   travel — travelled
   swim — swam
   play — played
   fall — fell
   leave — left

Punctuation

Section 6 – Sentence Punctuation

Pages 36 and 37 – Capital Letters for Names and I

1. You should have circled:
   geoffrey, italy, buckingham palace, april, thursday, mr smith

2. These are the phrases you should have ticked:
   my friend Jameela
   the train to London
   croissants from France
   football on Saturday
   These are the phrases you should have crossed and written out correctly:
   25 Church Street
   the book by Roald Dahl
   the beach in August
   Miss Hamilton's class

3. Last weekend, my brother **O**liver went hiking with his friends, **L**ydia and **M**arc. On **S**aturday, they climbed up **S**nowdon, the tallest mountain in **W**ales. Although it rained all day, they said that they had a great time. They want to go again in **S**eptember, but **I** won't go with them because **I** don't enjoy hiking.

4. Luckily, I asked Freida to help me.
   Miss Jones said I could be King John in the play.
   On Saturday, I watched England play football.
   Every June, I go camping in Ireland.

Pages 38 and 39 – Capital Letters and Full Stops

1. These are apple tarts. Those ones are lemon.
   Imran didn't go to school today. He was ill.
   I love maths. I don't like drawing.
   My mum's bike is black. My dad's is white.

2. The film is very funny.
   A mouse ate those biscuits.
   We got lost in the woods.

3. We finished the puzzle. It was easy.
   It was late. The shops were closing.
   My sister loves football. My dad prefers rugby.

4. Any sentence which starts with a capital letter and ends with a full stop. Examples:
   My house is in the countryside.
   I would really like a cheese sandwich.
   We watched the ballet at the theatre.
   My uncle drives a blue sports car.

Answers

5. Any sentence which starts with a capital letter and ends with a full stop. Examples:
My cousin has a pet lizard called Larry.
Karl thought the clown was a bit scary.
I've played the violin since I was five years old.

Pages 40 and 41 – Question Marks

1. I know who that is — full stop
What colour is your living room — question mark
Do you like reading — question mark
Which way should we go — question mark
I'll go if there's free ice cream — full stop

2. <u>Where</u> did you put my coat?
<u>What</u> is your brother's name?
<u>Why</u> are you telling me off?
<u>How</u> much fruit do you eat?
<u>Who</u> wants to play chess?
<u>When</u> is your birthday?

3. Where are my shoes?
What is the dog called?
Who won the race?
When did she arrive?

4. Any sensible question that is punctuated correctly. Examples:
What is your name?
When were you born?
Where do you live?

5. Any sentence which starts with a capital letter and ends with a question mark. Examples:
Would you like an apple or a slice of cake?
Do you come to school by bike or by car?
Have you seen the fair in the park?

Pages 42 and 43 – Exclamation Marks

1. We need to hide quickly!
Asher ordered a pizza and some garlic bread.
We've won the lottery!
Just leave your shoes by the door.
Ow, that hurts!
They thought about which film to watch.
There's a shark behind you!

2. You should have ticked:
Give me that now
Watch out
Stop fighting
Catch that thief

3. As soon as Dad stepped through the door, we all jumped out from our hiding places.
"Surprise!" we shouted.
"Blimey!" he exclaimed, putting his hand to his chest, "I nearly jumped out of my skin!"
"Happy birthday, Dad," I said, handing him his present.
"It's amazing!" he cried as he opened it.

4. Any sentence which should end in an exclamation mark. Examples:
"<u>Sit down at once</u>!" the witch snapped.
"<u>But I really want a pony</u>!" she cried.
"Hurry, Eva, before <u>someone sees us</u>!"
"If we wait any longer <u>we'll miss the show</u>!"
I screamed at the top of my lungs, "<u>Put that down</u>!"

5. Any sentence which starts with a capital letter and ends with an exclamation mark. Example:
I can't believe I won the race!

Pages 44 and 45 – Sentence Practice

1. Come here, right now — exclamation mark
What great news that is — exclamation mark
How do you get to school — question mark
What time is the film on — question mark
I'm playing football tonight — full stop
My mum's name is Rachel — full stop
I really can't believe it — exclamation mark

2. I'm going to Scotland on Friday.
There's a ghost in this house!
When is Nabila's birthday?
Was Catarina born in Portugal?
Mr Baker moved to Australia in May.

3. You've won!
Where are we going?
I'm friends with Anjali.
She crept down the stairs.
Custard is yellow.
Let me go!
Why did you leave?
Ow, that hurts!

4. "I opened my safe," the duke wailed, "and it was gone!"
The detective made a note in her notebook and looked at the duke. He was in his silk pyjamas, gently stroking his pet cat.
"Did anyone else know the code to the safe?" she asked.
"Only my butler," the duke said, "but why would he want to steal Fluffy's diamond collar?"

Answers

5. Any sentences which start with a capital letter and end with the correct piece of punctuation.
Examples:
Rob is very bored.
Rob is watching the television.
How do we get there?

Section 7 – Commas

Pages 46 and 47 – Writing Lists

1. You should have ticked:
Elena speaks English, Italian, Spanish and French.

2. Tyler loves to sing, act and dance.
Kofi's jumper is red, orange and yellow.
Nadeem never eats crisps, sweets or chocolate.

3. Emil needs to buy tomatoes, bananas, carrots and potatoes.

4. Are your eyes green, blue or brown?
The zoo has tigers, lions, zebras and rhinos.
Saskia likes to read, draw, paint and sew.

5. My best friends are Dylan, Nasir and Logan. Dylan is funny, friendly and chatty. Nasir is very sporty. He likes swimming, cycling and hockey. Logan likes animals. His family have cats, dogs and rabbits. He wants to be a vet when he grows up.

6. Any sentence where commas are used correctly.
Examples:
The socks are blue, green, white and spotty.
The kitten is small, fluffy, ginger and cute.

Pages 48 and 49 – Writing Longer Lists

1. I don't like eating my vegetables, doing my homework, cleaning my bedroom, going to bed early or getting up for school at 7 o'clock.

2. Yosef needs to buy a pint of milk, a bag of apples, a loaf of bread and a tin of baked beans.
I still need to have a wash, comb my hair, get dressed, eat my breakfast and brush my teeth.
Mia asked for a red mountain bike, a pair of trainers and a book about dinosaurs.
I watched a film, helped my mum make lunch, played with my brother and went to my gran's for tea.

3. For this recipe you will need 500 grams of sugar, half a dozen eggs, a kilogram of flour and a spoonful of honey.
In my beach bag I have a good book, a beach ball, a big towel and a bottle of sun-cream.

4. Any sentence where commas are used correctly.
Example:
This weekend I want to go to the beach, build a sand-castle, swim in the sea and eat an ice cream.

Section 8 – Apostrophes

Pages 50 and 51 – Apostrophes for Missing Letters

1. You should have matched these pairs:
I will — I'll
she had — she'd
he is — he's
they are — they're
we have — we've

2. was not — wasn't
it will — it'll
did not — didn't
that will — that'll
where is — where's
we are — we're

3. You should have put a cross next to these sentences:
My goats called Susan. (My goat's called Susan.)
His hamsters got spots. (His hamster's got spots.)
That rabbits got big ears. (That rabbit's got big ears.)
Your cats beautiful. (Your cat's beautiful.)

4. We will
does not
She is
They have

5. They're the best netball team.
It's raining and I'm getting wet.
That's the biggest cake I've ever seen.

Pages 52 and 53 – Apostrophes for Single Possession

1. Lucy's teddy bear
Elena's apple
Robert's grapes
Zahra's flower

2. You should have crossed out these phrases:
the cats
my sisters'
her friends

3. You should have ticked:
Thomas's painting is the best in the class.
The dress's stripes are blue and purple.

Answers

4. The man's house
   The cactus's spikes
   The castle's moat
   The suitcase's handles
   The bus's seats
   The bicycle's wheels
   The keyboard's keys

Pages 54 and 55 – Its and It's

1. You should have ticked:
   Oh no, <u>it's</u> a really hard maths test!
   The bird sang <u>its</u> happy song.
   I practise writing because <u>it's</u> tricky.

2. Do you think **it's** far to go?
   The bird flapped **its** wings.
   It's great to be on holiday.
   The cat licked **its** fur.
   The rat lost **its** way.
   I cant believe **it's** over.
   It's a big mess in here.
   The ant carried **its** leaf.

3. My hamster loves ___ ball. — its
   ___ all about taking part. — it's
   Well done, ___ going well. — it's
   The castle opened ___ gates. — its
   ___ been a very long day. — it's
   We should find ___ owner. — its
   ___ been ages since he left. — it's

4. Thank you, it's a lovely present. — it is
   It's been an awful weekend. — it has
   It's taken ages to make this cake. — it has
   I think it's going to snow today. — it is
   I love my jumper because it's warm. — it is
   I wonder if it's time to go home yet? — it is
   It's just begun to snow outside. — it has
   I can't believe it's only 8 o'clock! — it is

Pages 56 and 57 – Apostrophe Practice

1. Your table should look like this:

I am	I'm
you will	you'll
are not	aren't
we had	we'd
does not	doesn't
they have	they've

2. Lina's
   man's
   moon's
   Maria's

3. You should have ticked:
   You're my best friend.
   She's not very nice to me.
   It's been a great show.
   What's the time, please?

4. You should have added these apostrophes:
   Do you need Sam's help?
   This rug's got a nice pattern.
   This tin's lid is stuck.
   The exam's going to be fine.
   That plate's got egg on it.

5. The <u>door's</u> handle is broken. — to show possession
   My <u>hat's</u> bobbles are pink. — to show possession
   <u>When's</u> the circus coming? — for missing letters
   <u>It's</u> kind to share with others. — for missing letters

6. dog's
   I've
   you'll
   we'd

Section 9 – Inverted Commas

Pages 58 and 59 – Inverted Commas

1. You should have ticked these sentences:
   "Please may I have a sandwich?" asked Ava.
   "Add some salt to the soup," said the chef.

2. You should have added these inverted commas:
   "I've got new spotty wellies," said Nasreen.
   "Art is my favourite subject," said Bryony.
   "My mum's name is Jackie," I said.
   "Mushrooms are slimy and horrible," said Dan.
   "I'm going to explore the attic next," said Ruby.

3. You should have circled these inverted commas:
   "My mum is getting married," said Rosie.
   "When can we go outside?" asked Nasir.
   "We're having a party soon," said Alex.
   "Please can we have pasta for tea?" asked Maya.
   "Be careful with that!" shouted Mrs Wilkins.
   "Are you posting that letter?" asked David.

4. You should have added these inverted commas:
   "Can you give me some advice?" asked Noor.
   "I'm going to win the race," said Alison.
   "Yes, I'd love to go," replied Matteo.
   "There's a hole in my shoe!" said Kirsty.
   "Let's go and play in the snow," said Luca.

Answers

Pages 60 and 61 – Punctuating Speech

1. You should have circled these words:
   this
   you
   no
   excuse
   we

2. You should have ticked these sentences:
   "Have you put your shoes on yet?" I asked.
   Frankie said, "No, I haven't got any more."
   "I bet you can't catch me!" yelled Femi.

3. You should have added these inverted commas
   and then matched these pairs:
   Ben asked, "is this the way to the circus?" — I
   Emily said, "all the best players practise." — A
   Mikel replied, "yes, I would love to come." — Y
   Henry asked, "do I have to eat my apple?" — D
   Pasha said, "our dad is taking us to the ballet."
   — O

4. We said, "You can play with us if you don't
   cheat."
   The queen shouted, "Bring me my crown!"
   The girl asked, "Please may I have a go?"

Pages 62 and 63 – Direct and Reported Speech

1. I asked, "How are we getting there?"
   — direct speech
   Zack said he's playing rugby later.
   — reported speech
   "We had a quiet day," Jim told them.
   — direct speech
   I heard Laura say she would help me.
   — reported speech
   "I think we should take a break," I said.
   — direct speech

2. You should have ticked these sentences:
   Are you coming to the playground? asked Flora.
   ("Are you coming to the playground?" asked
   Flora.)
   Anya said, I've had a great idea for the fair.
   (Anya said, "I've had a great idea for the fair.")

3. Direct speech: "Are we there?"
   "Come here!"
   "I love you."
   Reported speech: Ron asked a question.
   George says he's tired.
   Luna talked a lot.

4. You should have added these inverted commas:
   "Yes, we have lots of crayons in the tin," said Dad.
   Luke said, "I'm learning to play the piano."
   "That was the best birthday ever!" I said happily.

Section 10 – Paragraphs and Layout

Pages 64 to 66 – Paragraphs

1. You should have ticked these reasons:
   When you're writing about a different time.
   When you're writing about a new place.
   When you're writing about a new person or
   subject.

2. Paragraphs have to start with 'and'. — false
   Paragraphs have to be two lines long. — false
   A new paragraph starts on a new line. — true
   Paragraphs are groups of sentences. — true
   Only use paragraphs when you want to. — false

3. person
   time
   subject

4. You should have added these three paragraph
   markers:
   A few months ago, Amal's mum took her to
   visit the zoo. She saw lions and tigers, as well
   as monkeys and bears. Amal thought it was
   amazing. // The next weekend Amal found out
   that the zoo wanted some school-children to start
   working there. She signed up straight away. //
   Now Amal goes along to the zoo every Saturday
   morning. She feeds the animals and helps to look
   after them. // Next month, Amal is going to be
   there when the new baby penguins are born. She
   can't wait!

5. You should have matched these pairs:
   Our family dog is called Rosie. — She is seven
   years old and loves to play catch.
   Last year I got a dress for my birthday. — It was
   green with a yellow flower pattern.
   Fred has ginger hair and brown eyes. — His older
   brother, George, has blue eyes.

6. You should have crossed the **first** and the **third**
   passages.

Page 67 – Headings and Subheadings

1. You should have ticked these statements:
   A heading tells you the main subject of the text.
   Subheadings break up a text into smaller sections.

Answers

2. You should have matched these pairs:
Fish and chips — Deep-fried fish served with chips. Usually served as take-away food with salt and vinegar.
Sticky Toffee Pudding — A steamed pudding made with sponge, dates and toffee sauce. Often served with custard.
English Breakfast — Eggs, bacon, sausages, beans and toast. Often served all day — not just for breakfast.

Spelling

Section 11 – Prefixes

Pages 68 and 69 – Prefixes – 'un', 'dis' and 'mis'

1. **un** + known, **mis** + print, **dis** + approve, **un** + even
2. **unaware, unequal, disregard, unpaid, misbehave**
3. You should have underlined: **diskind, discalculate, unspell** and **misappoint**.
The correct spellings are: **unkind, miscalculate, misspell** and **disappoint**.
4. **disown, mistreat, mismatch, dismiss, displease, disagree**
5. **un**well, **un**locked, **dis**appeared, **mis**understood, **un**packed

Page 70 – Prefixes – 're' and 'anti'

1. **anti**clockwise, **anti**septic, **re**charge, **re**fresh, **re**write, **anti**climax, **re**create, **re**heat, **re**design
2. **reapply, antibiotic, reopen, antivirus, resend, return**

Page 71 – Prefixes – 'sub' and 'super'

1. **submarine, superglue, supermarket, superhero**
2. **sub**merge, **super**sonic, **sub**divided, **sub**heading
3. Any correctly spelt words that start with the correct prefixes.
Examples:
supervision, supersize, superpower, superstar sublet, sublevel, subtotal, subtitles

Section 12 – Suffixes and Word Endings

Pages 72 and 73 – Suffixes – 'ing' and 'ed'

1. **hunting, hunted
jumping, jumped
treating, treated**
2. perform**ing**, entertain**ed**, deliver**ing**
3. **shopping, struggling, employed, enjoyed, carried, stopped, celebrating**
4. You should have underlined: **worryed, balanceing, hurryed, cryed**.
The correct spellings are: **worried, balancing, hurried, cried**.

Pages 74 and 75 – Suffixes – 'er' and 'est'

1. **older, fewer, smaller, taller
oldest, fewest, smallest, tallest**
2. cold**er**, cold**est**, fast**est**, rich**er**
3. sing**er**, garden**er**, teach**er**, bank**er**, plumb**er**, wait**er**
4. **nastier, voter, spicier, tiniest, dancer, buyer, fatter, easiest**
5. You should have circled: **funnyest, manageer, shinyer, bikeers, muddyest**.
The correct spellings are: **funniest, manager, shinier, bikers, muddiest**.

Pages 76 and 77 – Suffixes – 'ment', 'ness', 'ful' and 'less'

1. **fearful, sadness, enjoyment, stressful, playful**
2. **spotless, equipment, brightness**
3. **beautiful, penniless, laziness, bumpiness, merciful, happiness, merriment**
4. mercy — **merciless**, easy — **easiness**, hope — **hopeless**, care — **careful**, place — **placement**

Pages 78 and 79 – Suffixes – 'ation' and 'ous'

1. **plantation, famous, publication**
2. You should have underlined: **celebrateion, glamourous, locateation,**
The correct spellings are: **celebration, glamorous, location,**
3. **preparation, invitation, outrageous**
4. mountain**ous**, danger**ous**, inform**ation**, hazard**ous**, expect**ation**
5. **hilarious, courageous, glamorous, infectious**

Answers

Pages 80 and 81 – Suffixes – 'ly'

1. **angrily, rudely, simply, gently**
2. **deadly, busily, frantically, gladly, nobly**
3. You should have ticked: **boldly, badly, softly, calmly, meanly.**
   You should have crossed: **cuddlely, sensiblely, humblely, subtlely.**
   The correct spellings are: cuddly, sensibly, humbly, subtly.
4. **warmly, slightly, ably**
5. Any words ending in -ly that are spelt correctly.
   Examples:
   smoothly, quietly, loudly, proudly

Pages 82 and 83 – Word Endings – 'sure' and 'ture'

1. **picture, measure, gesture, nature, pleasure**
2. **enclosure, manufacture, composure, mixture, structure, treasure**
3. **leisure, torture, creature**
4. **treasure, furniture, temperature, composure, adventure**
5. Any words ending in -sure or -ture that are spelt correctly.
   Examples:
   closure, unsure, assure, ensure, pressure, reassure
   capture, feature, posture, nurture, culture

Section 13 – Confusing Words

Page 84 – The Short 'i' Sound

1. Words with a short 'i' sound: **spill, gym, rapid, system**
   Words with a long 'i' sound: **nice, pine, wire, wife**
2. **wish, tiger, chin, time, crypt**
3. insect, panic, gift, crystal, syrup, mystery, satisfy, since

Page 85 – The Hard 'c' Sound

1. atta**ck**, wal**k**ing, **c**offee, **k**itten, **c**ri**ck**et, do**ct**or
2. **castle, duck**
3. homesi**ck**, o**ct**opus, skeleton

Page 86 – The Soft 'c' Sound

1. **sentence, space, excited, pencil**
2. **grace, absent, justice, icy, cancel, insist**
3. sen**c**e, a**c**id, dan**c**e, spi**c**y, de**c**ent, house, chase, upset

Page 87 – The 'sh' Sound

1. **sh**oe, para**ch**ute, **s**ugar, **sh**ark
2. **machine, tissue, shampoo, brochure**
3. **ashamed, pressure**

Page 88 – The 'ay' Sound

1. **afraid, brave, anyway, essay**
2. **sailor, grapes, calculate**
3.

Page 89 – Word Families

1. **frosting, frosted, defrost, frostbite**
2. face: **deface, preface, facing**
   move: **remove, movement**
   trust: **distrust, trustworthy, trusted**
3. Any correctly spelt words from the correct word family.
   Examples:
   taking, retake
   dated, outdated
   doing, undo

Pages 90 and 91 – Plurals

1. chur**ches**, piano**s**, key**s**, potato**es**, box**es**
2. pon**ies**, lea**ves**, difficult**ies**, shop**s**, torch**es**, bucket**s**, wol**ves**, thie**ves**, apolog**ies**, shel**ves**, fox**es**, pencil**s**
3. **geese, mice, reflexes, elves, women**
4. **teeth, halves, cliffs**

Answers

5. Any sentence containing the correct plural.
   Examples:
   The **donkeys** were tired after their long journey.
   We had ham **sandwiches** for lunch.
   I baked three **batches** of cookies.

Pages 92 and 93 – Possessive Apostrophes

1. You should have crossed: **Peter's kitten's**, **Gemmas' bat, Jeremys' pens**
   The correct phrases are: Peter's kitten**s**, Gemma**'s** bat, Jeremy**'s** pens

2. You should have underlined: **Judiths, Mums, Matts, Jackies, Kevins**
   The correct spellings are: Judith's, Mum's, Matt's, Jackie's, Kevin's.

3. **It's** your turn to do the washing-up.
   The gorilla beat **its** chest to scare **its** rival.
   Mr Chen's cat ate all of **its** food straight away.

4. the pirate's ship, the cleaner's mop

5. Any sentences that use possessive apostrophes correctly.
   Examples:
   My grandma's name is Jeanne.
   Thomas's football kit was very dirty.
   The parrot's claws were very sharp.

Pages 94 and 95 – Homophones

1. **mane, bee, bear, sun**

2. Vegetarians don't eat **meat**.
   Where shall we **meet**?
   I can't **accept** this.
   I like all vegetables **except** carrots.
   Don't **break** anything.
   Make sure you **brake** at the corner.

3. Becky and Habiba dyed **their** hair the same colour.
   Are **there** any biscuits left in the tin?
   Three people said **they're** coming to my party.

4. You should have written: **rain, hear, deer, made**

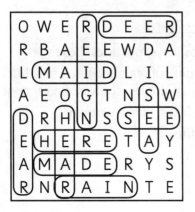

5. Any sentence where the word is used correctly.
   Examples:
   I am going **to** Oxford.
   There are **two** sides to the argument.
   I like that one **too**.

Section 14 – Mixed Spelling Practice

Pages 96 to 98 – Mixed Spelling Practice

1. **un + paid, sub + category, mis + trust, re + cycle**

2. **busier, busiest, busying, busied**
   happiest, happily, happier, happiness

3. You should have circled: **merryment, usualy, disimilar, angryly, picsure**
   The correct spellings are: **merriment, usually, dissimilar, angrily, picture**

4. ba**ck**, loo**k**, sket**ch**, tal**k**, **c**ook, ro**ck**et

5. **mystery, chalet, weight, machine, They, myth**

6. **countries, boxes, thieves, potatoes**

7. You should have crossed: **Andys' hat, Ruths' mug, Lily's cat's**

8. Across clues: 1. **neck** 2. **misbehave** 3. **once** 4. **tricks**
   Down clues: 1. **neighbour** 2. **subway**

9. Any sentence where the words are used correctly.
   Examples:
   I went to a **sale** and bought a **sail**.
   I have a problem with my left **eye**.